MY BIG TOE

BOOK 3:

INNER WORKINGS

Section 5
Inner Space, the Final Frontier:
The Mechanics of Nonphysical Reality – A Model

Section 6
The End is Always the Beginning
Today is the First Day of the Rest of Your Existence

The *My Big TOE* reality model will help you understand your life, your purpose, the totality of the reality you experience, how that reality works, and how you might interact most profitably with it.

A half dozen independent test readers of various backgrounds were asked to evaluate the My Big TOE *trilogy and record their impressions of it. This is what they said:*

■ ■ ■

"Eureka! A Theory Of Everything that actually lives up to its name! *My Big TOE* not only unifies physics, but unifies philosophy and theology as well. You will be amazed!"
— PAMELA KNIGHT, PHYSICIST

"Reading *My Big TOE* has challenged my mind and widened my horizon. Expect your worldview to radically expand and your perspective to reach a new level of understanding."
— INA KUZMAN

"*My Big TOE* is utterly original, pioneering and bold. Campbell writes with clarity and humor as he explores and answers the hard questions in this comprehensive work about the ultimate nature of reality and consciousness. Full of fresh and profound ideas, you may be astonished to find that learning how reality works actually improves the quality of your life."
— LYLE FULLER, POWER ENGINEER

"The *My Big TOE* trilogy roared through my comfy no-brainer world like a category F5 tornado that makes you laugh ... when the dust finally settled, I was left with an incredibly clear view of how and why things are as they are."
— PEG ROCHINE, FOUNDER AND CEO, CLINICAL RESEARCH

"This trilogy will profoundly change you .... you will never look at your world in the same way again."
— INA KUZMAN

"Thoroughly challenging, engaging ... a transforming experience. *My Big TOE* marks the end of humanity's childhood."
— LYLE FULLER, POWER ENGINEER

"Unique, profound, and enriching are the words that most easily come to my mind to describe *My Big TOE.*"
— TREVOR GOLDSTEIN, PHILOSOPHER AND FUTURIST

"If you have ever asked the questions: Is this all there is?, What's the purpose?, How am I related to the whole?, *My Big TOE's* logic, grounded in science, provides unequivocal answers that make you think. A profoundly fascinating read!"
— INA KUZMAN

MY BIG TOE

A TRILOGY
UNIFYING PHILOSOPHY,
PHYSICS, AND METAPHYSICS

BOOK 1:
AWAKENING

BOOK 2:
DISCOVERY

BOOK 3:
INNER WORKINGS

Thomas Campbell

Find the other two books of the *My Big TOE* trilogy:
http://www.My-Big-TOE.com
http://www.lightningstrikebooks.com
Phone orders: 1 – 800 – 901 – 2122

MY BIG TOE: A TRILOGY UNIFYING PHILOSOPHY, PHYSICS, AND METAPHYSICS

BOOK 3: INNER WORKINGS

Lightning Strike Books
http://www.LightningStrikeBooks.com

Printed in the United States of America
First Edition: February, 2003

Book design by Michele DeFilippo, 1106 Design, LLC
Cover illustration by Frank Foster

Publishers Catalogue-in-Publication Data
Campbell, Thomas
My Big TOE: Inner Workings. Book 3 of a trilogy unifying philosophy, science, and metaphysics / Thomas Campbell
1. Science. 2. Philosophy. 3. Metaphysics. 4. Reality, model of.
5. Consciousness, theory of. 6. Spirituality. 7. Paranormal, theory of.
8. Theory of Everything. 9. TOE. 10. Theology (religion) and science.

ISBN 0-9725094-4-5 (Softcover)
ISBN 0-9725094-5-3 (Hardcover)

To Chris

To Bob & Nancy

To Dennis & Nancy Lea

To Todd, Lyle, Ina, and Trevor,
whose encouragement
was key to success

To those in need of
a new perspective

To all seekers of Big Truth

To Pamela, The One

To love within
A joyous
Heart

■■■

Synopsis
My Big Picture
Theory of Everything

**My Big TOE – A trilogy unifying
philosophy physics, and metaphysics**

■■■

Book 1: Awakening

Section 1 provides a partial biography of the author that is pertinent to the subsequent creation of this trilogy. This brief look at the author's unique experience and credentials sheds some light upon the origins of this extraordinary work. The unusual associations, circumstances, training and initial research that eventually led to the creation of the *My Big TOE* trilogy are described to provide a more accurate perspective of the whole.

Section 2 lays out, logically justifies, and defines the basic conceptual building blocks needed to construct *My Big TOE*'s conceptual foundation. It discusses the cultural beliefs that trap our thinking into a narrow and limited conceptualization of reality, defines the fundamentals of Big Picture epistemology and ontology, as well as examines the inner-workings and practice of meditation. Most importantly, Section 2 defines and develops the two basic assumptions upon which this trilogy is based. From these two assumptions, time, space, consciousness, and the basic properties, purpose, and mechanics of our reality is logically inferred.

Book 2: Discovery

Section 3 develops the interface and interaction between "we the people" and our digital consciousness reality. It derives and explains the characteristics, origins, dynamics, and function of ego, love, free will, and our larger purpose. Finally, Section 3 develops the psi uncertainty principle as it explains and interrelates psi phenomena, free will, love, consciousness evolution, physics, reality, human purpose, digital computation, and entropy.

Section 4 describes an operational and functional model of consciousness that further develops the results of Section 3 and supports the conclusions of Section 5. The origins and nature of digital consciousness are described along with how artificial intelligence (AI), as embodied in AI Guy, leads to artificial consciousness, which leads to actual consciousness and to us. Section 4 derives our physical universe, our science, and our perception of a physical reality. The mind-matter dichotomy is solved as physical reality is directly derived from the nature of digital consciousness.

Book 3: Inner Workings

Section 5 pulls together Sections 2, 3, and 4 into a more formal model of reality that describes how an apparent nonphysical reality works, interacts, and interrelates with our experience of physical reality. Probable realities, predicting and modifying the future, teleportation, telepathy, multiple physical and nonphysical bodies, and the fractal nature of an evolving digital consciousness reality are explained and described in detail.

Section 6 is the wrap-up that puts everything discussed in Sections 2, 3, 4, and 5 into an easily understood personal perspective. Additionally, Section 6 points out *My Big TOE*'s relationship with contemporary science and philosophy. By demonstrating a close conceptual relationship between this TOE and some of the establishment's biggest intellectual guns, Section 6 solidly integrates *My Big TOE* into traditional Western scientific and philosophical thought.

Contents

BOOK 3: Inner Workings

SECTION 5
Inner Space, the Final Frontier:

Acknowledgements

The One. In a category all to herself, I wish to acknowledge the immeasurable contribution, in all possible forms, given by my most constant, consistent, and challenging teacher: Pamela – The One.

Fellow travelers. First and foremost, acknowledgement goes to Bob Monroe and his wife Nancy who enabled my exploration of the path that eventually led to the *My Big TOE* trilogy. Next, to Dennis Mennerich, my fellow explorer and traveling companion. We pulled each other along when neither of us knew much about where we were going or how we were going to get there. Then, to Nancy Lea McMoneagle who was not only a fellow traveler but also the primary enabler of Monroe's success. All gems, every one – I could not possibly have set out on this strange journey with a better collection of friends and mentors. Finally, to the un-named many who provided me with the opportunities that enabled me to be what and who I have become. I wish I could have made more of the opportunities you offered. In the end it is these tens, these hundreds, these thousands, who made this trilogy possible. Thank you all.

Major contributors. In a more direct and immediate vein, there are a few readers of indomitable fortitude to whom I am eternally grateful. The time and effort volunteered by these remarkable people made all the difference in the world. Together we have tried hard to make all three books as clear and understandable as possible.

Special thanks go to Lyle Fuller, Todd Phillips, Ina Kuzman, and Caroline Lampert for their effort to improve the readability and clarity of *My Big TOE*. All three were quick to point out where I had left stumbling blocks lying on the path to Big TOE understanding. Additionally, Todd's and Ina's questions served as a catalyst to ferret out much interesting material. Many thanks to Chris Nelson who started me writing in the first place. Without their selfless generosity and dedication beyond all reason, this trilogy would be a poor shadow of what you have before you.

In addition, I thank Nancy Lea McMoneagle and Dennis Mennerich for aiding and corroborating the accuracy of my memories of the early years at Whistlefield. Also heartfelt thanks to Lyle Fuller, Joel Dobrzelewski, Trevor Goldstein, and Eric Campbell for their encouragement and good questions. Special thanks to Steve Tragesser for asking questions that became the catalyst for much of Chapter 18, Book 3. Likewise, to Lyle Fuller for doggedly pursuing questions that eventually produced the discussion of free will found in Chapter 11, Book 2 and that added clarity to my exposition of the psi uncertainty principle. Similarly, to Trevor Goldstein whose experience and questions precipitated the discussion of mind tectonics in Chapter 6, Book 2; and to Ina Kuzman for initiating the discussion found in Chapter 23, Book 1 about the nature and practice of meditation. Also, thanks goes to Eric Campbell for precipitating a discussion about the natural constraints of a finite consciousness system. Credit goes to Tom Hand, Zane Young, Rhonda Ganz, and Kristopher Campbell for offering useful suggestions and comments. Finally, I wish to thank Steve Kaufman for being in the right place at the right time with his book, *Unified Reality Theory: The Evolution of Existence Into Experience*. I love it when a plan comes together.

Hired Help. Two ladies of great integrity and competency enabled *My Big TOE* to make the transition from an amateur creation to a professional product. Kate von Seeburg, owner of *K8 & Company*, edited the manuscript while Michele DeFilippo, owner of *1106 Design*, produced the interior and cover designs.

Family. Great appreciation goes to my wife and children, who patiently and cheerfully allowed me to work on "the book" when I should have been paying attention to them. I hope the final result will prove itself worthy of our collective sacrifice.

Non-contributors. Last, and certainly least, I wish to barely mention Kathy Cyphert and Peggy Rochine, who, along with many others too numerous to name, contributed absolutely nothing to this effort but wanted to see their names mentioned in it just the same. Additionally, Boldar, Kiana, Onyx, Joe, Nikki, Chico, Mr. Pickle, Sid, Moe, Sir Maximus, Snuffy, Sir Minimus, Kia, Gabrielle, Isabel, and Kuga-Bear also deserve honorable mentions as outstanding non-contributors.

—Tom Campbell,
Dec. 9, 2002

■ ■ ■

Preface: Author's Note to the Reader

■ ■ ■

Yes, you should read this preface.

I understand that many readers have little interest in, or patience for, lengthy prefaces or forewords. The first question is always: Should I take the time to read this ancillary text, or can I skip it without missing anything important?

Most of us are eager to zip past the preliminaries and immediately sink our teeth into the meat of the main text. Anticipation and expectation push us to get on with the real thing. We of Western culture are an impatient goal oriented people driven toward endpoints. In our rush to the finish line, we take little notice of the journey that gets us there. Such a misappropriation of emphasis often squanders our opportunities because, more often than not, the tastiest and most nourishing part of life lies in experiencing the process, not in attaining the goal.

By the end of Section 6, you will no doubt agree that these books are ... well ...different. As such, they require a different approach. The preface and foreword of the *MY Big TOE* trilogy **are** integral parts of the story. Because this trilogy blazes an original trail far off the beaten path, it is essential to include introductory material that can help prepare you for what lies ahead. I know you are eager to get on with it and discover if this trilogy delivers the goods, but rushing off toward that goal too quickly actually reduces the likelihood that you will get there at all.

The function of the preface and the foreword is to maximize the return on your reading investment. The preface provides an overview of the tone, structure, process, and mechanics of the *My Big TOE* trilogy. The foreword establishes a broad view of the trilogy's content and lays out a rough map of where you will be going on this unusual journey. It provides the context and focus wherein the trilogy's content is most easily understood. The foreword and preface together improve comprehension and minimize frustration by providing a global view of the forest before you begin your descent into the trees.

I strongly suggest that you adopt an attitude of patience toward gaining an understanding of the profound mysteries and ancient secrets that are logically unraveled by this new physics. My Big Picture Theory Of Everything (*My Big TOE*) will take you to both the beginning and to the end of time. It will dive deeply into the human heart as well as probe the limits of the human mind. It will define the significance of you, and provide new meaning to your existence. It will help you realize and optimize your potential. It will develop a wholly new scientific understanding of both your inside and outside world.

You may find it more productive to pace yourself by depth of comprehension than by percent of completion. Avoid rushing from concept to concept the way children pursue presents on Christmas day. Take your time. A feast for heart, head, and soul is best ingested little by little, bite by bite, with many thoughtful pauses and much careful cogitation to aid digestion. Genuine breakthroughs must be absorbed slowly as existing paradigms grudgingly dissolve. Familiar paradigms, like a favorite teddy bear, can be extremely difficult to let go.

Every successful journey, regardless of how long or difficult, begins with a single step that is animated by gumption, directed by goals, and repeated as often as necessary by dogged perseverance. On this particular journey, the preface is located at step one, the foreword at step two, followed by the three books: *Awakening, Discovery*, and *Inner Workings*.

I have carefully aimed the content of this scientific and philosophic exposition at a general audience of varied background. You do not need a scientific, philosophical, or metaphysical background to understand the content of the My Big Picture Theory Of Everything trilogy. No leaps of faith or beliefs are required to get to where these books will take you. A determined and tenacious truth seeker – a sturdy, independent intellect that is by nature open minded and skeptical – constitutes the optimal reader. There are no prerequisites. If you have a logical, open, and inquisitive mind – an attitude of scientific pragmatism that appreciates the elegance of fundamental truth and the thrill of breakthrough – you will enjoy this journey of personal and scientific discovery.

Under the best of circumstances the successful communication of this trilogy's content will require much from both of us. This work presents many unique and daunting challenges to the effective communication between author and reader. Worldviews are not casually picked, like fruit, from a vendor's cart: To make the necessary connections, we must dive deeply.

Far beneath the foundation of your intellect, your culture lays out the template for your worldview upon the core belief systems that define your perception of existence. The basic assumptions that support your notion of reality are not seen by you as assumptions at all – they are accepted, without question, as the most solid of all facts. That is simply the nature of culture – belief at the bone and sinew level of awareness. The point is: The concepts presented by this trilogy are likely to challenge the belief systems of your culture – regardless of what culture you come from.

Material within *My Big TOE* may challenge your familiar assumptions, beliefs, and paradigms to the point of serious discomfort. If that discomfort leads to a profitable resolution, I am pleased; if it does not, I am saddened. My goal is to be informative and helpful. I encourage you to take what you can profitably use and leave the rest.

There are enough new concepts and unusual perspectives presented here to support and generate a multitude of books. I have purposely left much unsaid at the periphery in order to stay focused on the central idea of developing a Big TOE. Though the trilogy remains, from beginning to end, tightly focused on its primary objective, I will occasionally take short side trips in the form of asides to add color, explore related connections, and insert topics of special interest and practical value. Hopefully, you will find these side trips so interesting and informative that you will gladly excuse their interruption. Some effort will be required on your part to bridge these asides in order to maintain the logical continuity of the larger discussion. To make sure that you are never confused about whether you are reading an aside or the main text, asides are indented, have their own special font, and are clearly marked (at the beginning and end) with dingbats that look like this: ▶. If a secondary aside resides within a primary aside, it is indented yet again and marked with double dingbats ▶▶. When an aside fills an entire page, it is difficult to judge how much the text is indented, consequently, when this condition occurs, dingbats are placed in the header to let you know that the text is part of an aside. Thus, a casual glance is all that is required to determine if the text that you are reading is part of an aside, and if so, at what level.

You may find the text to be challenging in some places and obvious in others. What is too challenging or too obvious to each reader is mostly dependent on the experience and understanding of that individual reader.

It is my intent to never speed through this exposition at such a rate that you cannot appreciate the scenery, nor to wallow about repetitively in the obvious – though from time to time, depending on your background, some may feel that I occasionally do both.

Although the language of American English (the language in which these books were originally written) is decidedly poor in nonphysical conceptual descriptors, it does have the advantage of being unusually rich in communications and information technology descriptors. The latter, oddly enough, is what allows me to convey the former. As strange as that may seem, it is the pervasiveness of modern science and technology, especially communications and data processing technology, that provides the conceptual tools required to produce a model of the larger reality the Western mind – or more broadly, the Western attitude or more accurately, the Western belief system – can relate to, understand, and work with.

Science and technology have advanced to the point where their applications and understanding have begun to mirror some of the fundamental processes of existence. We of the twenty-first century have only recently acquired the necessary concepts to understand and appreciate the nature of the larger reality within the context of our contemporary Western point of view. Previously, knowledge and understanding of the Big Picture and our existence in it was comprehended and described by ancient sages in terms of metaphors that were pertinent to their cultures and specifically created for the benefit of their specific audiences. Today, we find these once practical descriptions to be largely symbolic and irrelevant to a modern scientific view of reality. Philosophy, theology, and science find themselves at odds over what is significant.

I am a scientist. This trilogy is the result of a long and careful scientific exploration focused upon the nature of reality and the individual. Preconceived notions will be more of a hindrance than a help. It is the task of this trilogy to clearly and completely construct your consciousness, your world, your science, and your existence in a general, logical, scientific way that comprehensively explains **all** the personal and professional data you have collected during a lifetime. An overarching Big Picture theory that explains **everything** may seem highly unlikely, if not absolutely impossible, but it is not. Take heart: Good science and human ingenuity have consistently delivered the impossible for at least two hundred years. Be open – history repeatedly demonstrates that the appearance of impossibility is most often the result of limited vision.

Patience will be required. This adventure of mind, science, and spirit is complex and will take significant time to properly unfold. If it were immediately obvious, it would either be old news or you would be reading a short journal article instead of a trilogy. A keen mind that is skeptical and open is the only ticket you need to take this journey.

Based on the feedback from those who have preceded you, I expect that you will find this voyage into the depths of elemental consciousness and fundamental reality to be personally enriching. You will be pushed to think a few big thoughts and ponder a few big ideas, but the conclusions you eventually come away with will be entirely yours, not mine. These are not books that set out to convince you of anything, or persuade you towards a particular point of view. At every turn you are strongly dissuaded from becoming a believer. Data, facts, and measurable results are the exclusive currency upon which this trilogy trades.

Reading the *My Big TOE* trilogy is not likely to be a passive experience. If you decide to seize the opportunity to climb out of the box, you will likely end up doing some difficult work. You will always be encouraged to think for yourself and come to conclusions that are based on **your** personal experience. Despite all the serious cogitation, we are also going to play, laugh, and have some fun as we go.

Much of what you believe to be true about yourself, your existence, and the nature of reality will be challenged. If you are open to exploring a bigger picture, these books will make you think, and think again. Most readers will not consider this trilogy to be an easy read – merely following the logical processes and sequences as they swallow up old paradigms will require some focused effort. On the other hand, significant growth and learning is rarely easy – if easy, it is rarely significant.

Contrary to my best efforts, Sections 2, 3, 4 and 5 remain somewhat conceptually interdependent. Each section will be better understood and make much more sense after reading the other sections. That could not be helped. Reality is a unified whole thing with each of its parts inexorably intertwined with the others.

This trilogy's three books and six sections develop the conceptual content of *My Big TOE* more or less sequentially. Consequently, reading the books or sections out of numerical order provides a less than optimal experience. However, understanding *My Big TOE* is much more dependent upon reading the entire trilogy than it is upon reading it in any particular order.

The nature of reality and of the typical reader is such that we must sneak up on *My Big TOE* one concept at a time. We will examine the Big Picture from multiple perspectives to ensure the design and structure of the whole becomes clearly visible. If things seem to get a little far out every once in a while, hang tough until it all pulls together into a coherent complete picture.

For the reasons stated above, a slow and careful reading will optimize your investment – take your time, and meander through these books at a relaxed and unhurried pace. If you become bogged down, it is better to go on (and come back later if you want to) than to feel as if you must read every word in the order in which it appears. It would be unfortunate for you to miss seeing a part of the forest that may be important to you because you became lost, exhausted, or discouraged wandering unproductively among the trees in another part.

Throughout *My Big TOE*, I have used a seeding technique to sneak up on some of the more difficult ideas. I often plant conceptual seeds (that briefly bring up or introduce an idea) within the sections, chapters, pages, or paragraphs that precede a full and thorough discussion of that idea. I do this because many readers will find the concepts presented within *My Big TOE* to be totally unfamiliar. Comprehension and understanding of this trilogy is significantly improved if the reader is at least somewhat prepared for the major conceptual discussions.

Questions may occasionally leap into your mind as you read. Hold on to your questions, or better yet, write them down as you go. Most will be answered within a few paragraphs or pages. If you have unanswered questions after completing Section 5, these can be productively used as the initial focus of your own quest for Big Truth – a subject that is taken up with gusto in Section 6.

Be careful not to lose sight of the Big Picture as a result of being overly focused on the details. It is easy to get twisted around details that strike an emotive resonance with your beliefs. The winning strategy here is to get a glimpse of the entire forest, not to argue about the color of the moss growing on specific trees. Control your passionate interest in the coloration of moss or you may entirely miss what is important.

One final note before you begin. Those who know me well, along with a few of the initial readers, have suggested that I forewarn you about my sense of humor. If you read something in these books that could be interpreted as humor, sarcasm, condescension, arrogance, silliness, inanity, or all of the above, it is probably only humor, or occasionally, humor with a touch of sarcasm. If you find yourself unsure of how offended you should be, I suggest that you temporarily suspend your judgment of the author's mind-set. I am told that eventually (by the end of Section 4) you'll be familiar with my stealthy humor and informal chatty style. Consequently, a later judgment may be more accurate.

The structural anatomy of *My Big TOE* is laid open like a frog on the dissecting table in the paragraphs below. Most readers will find that this overview provides a helpful perspective on how the book you are now reading fits into the overall *My Big TOE* trilogy.

My Big TOE is designed as a three book trilogy. It is packaged as separate books for those who are not sure of how big a bite they wish to take, and as a more economical three book set for those who are confident they want it all. Each book contains the identical dedication, synopsis, table of contents, acknowledgements, preface, and foreword, as well as its own acronym list and two unique sections of content. Though the table of contents displays the contents of all three books a the beginning of each book, the contents belonging to the other two books are cast in light grey instead of black. Although chapter and page numbering starts anew within each book, the six sections are numbered sequentially across the entire trilogy to add a sense of structural continuity.

Book 1: *Awakening* contains the first two sections. **Section 1** provides a partial biography of the author that is pertinent to the subject matter. Its function is to shed light on the origins of this unusual work by providing a look at the author's unique experiences and credentials that eventually led to the creation of *My Big TOE*. **Section 2** lays out the basic building blocks needed to develop this TOE's conceptual foundation. Many of the concepts initiated in Section 2 will be more fully explored in later sections.

Book 2: *Discovery* contains the middle two sections. **Section 3** takes the information gained in Section 2 and develops its implications in more detail and depth while relating it more directly to the reader's personal experience. **Section 4** pulls together the ideas of Sections 2 and 3, while developing the additional concepts required to bind it all together into one consistent whole. Sections 2, 3, and 4 are carefully designed to sequentially work together to produce the fundamental understanding that is necessary to comprehend Section 5.

Book 3: *Inner Workings* contains the last two sections. **Section 5** presents the formal reality model in detail. **Section 6** is the wrap-up that puts everything discussed into an easily understood perspective. Additionally, Section 6 points out *My Big TOE's* relationship with contemporary science and philosophy. By demonstrating a close conceptual relationship between this TOE and some of the establishment's biggest scientific and philosophic intellectual guns, Section 6 integrates *My Big TOE* into traditional Western science and philosophy.

There is a place in cyberspace [**http://www.My-Big-TOE.com** This URL is not case sensitive but the **hyphens are required**] set aside for you to share your experience, exercise your intellect, voice your opinions, vent your angst, or simply hang out with your fellow travelers. You can send email to both the author and the publisher from the **my-big-toe.com** web site, as well as acquire all Big TOE books. There, you can keep up with the latest in Big TOE info, happenings, chitchat, reviews, research, and discussion groups.

— Tom Campbell

Dec. 9, 2002

Foreword: A Conceptual Orientation

Without the proper perspective, clear vision produces only data. The point here is to give the reader an initial high altitude peek at the forest before we begin our trek into its depths. In this foreword, I will describe where you will be going and what you should expect to accomplish. It is always helpful to know where you are headed even if you have no idea of how you are going to get there. This conceptual fly-over is designed to minimize the disorienting affect of totally unfamiliar territory.

Both the structure and the content of your perception of reality are culturally dependent. How a Tibetan Buddhist monk or an American physicist would describe reality is as vastly different as the words, expressions, and metaphors that each would employ to make such a description. What would make sense and be obvious to one would seem to be lost and out of touch to the other. If we can rise above our cultural bias, we have a tendency to ask, or at least wonder: Which description is right and which one is wrong? They seem clearly incompatible – certainly both could not be equally accurate and correct. If we are more sophisticated, we might ask which portions of each description are right or wrong and search for areas of possible agreement as well as define areas that appear to be mutually exclusive. That is a better approach, but it is still wrong-headed.

Neither of the above approaches, though the second is much more expansive than the first, will find truth. Which is right or wrong is the wrong question – it represents a narrow and exclusive perspective. Which works, which helps its owner to better attain his or her goals, which goals are more productive and lead to growth and progress of the individual – to happiness, satisfaction and usefulness to others? These are somewhat better questions because they focus on practical results and on the measurable effects that each worldview has when applied to individuals – as well as the secondary effects those individuals have on others. However, something important is missing. How does one define, realize, and measure the satisfaction, personal growth, quality of life, and fulfillment of individual purpose that is derived from each worldview? What is the standard against which the achievement of these goals is assessed? Now we have a set of questions that have the potential to lead to personal discovery in pursuit of fundamental truth. Big Picture Significance and value have replaced little picture right and wrong as the primary measure of worth. Fundamental truth (Big Picture Truth or simply Big Truth), though absolute and uniformly significant to everyone, must be discovered by each individual within the context of that individual's experience. No one approach to that discovery is the right one for everybody. The significance of "little truth," on the other hand, is circumstantial and relative to the observer.

Truth exists in all cultures. It is only understandable to an individual when it is expressed in the language (symbols, metaphors, and concepts) of that individual. It is the intent of *My Big TOE* to capture the scientific and metaphysical truth from multiple cultures and multiple disciplines and present them within one coherent, self-consistent model that the objective Western mind can easily comprehend. After all, a TOE (Theory Of Everything) must contain and explain **everything**. That is a tall order. A Big Picture Theory Of Everything or Big TOE must include metaphysics (ontology, epistemology, and cosmology) as well as physics and the other sciences within a single seamless integrated model of reality. That is what the *My Big TOE* trilogy is all about.

Truth is truth, but communicating a truth to another is a difficult undertaking fraught with misunderstandings of meaning and interpretation. Big Truth, like wisdom, is not something you can teach or learn from a book. It must be comprehended by individuals within the context of their experience. Each of us comes to an understanding of reality through our interpretation of our physical and mental experiences.

The experience of others can at best provide a useful model – a framework for understanding – a perspective that enables us to comprehend and interpret our experience data in a way that makes good practical sense. The best teachers can do no more than offer a consistent and coherent understanding of reality that helps their students find the larger perspective required to self-discover Big Truth. Such a model is only correct and comprehensive if it accurately describes all the data (physics and metaphysics) all the time under all circumstances for everyone who applies it. The usefulness of a model depends on how correctly it describes the data of experience. A good model should be predictive. It should explain what is known, produce useful new knowledge, and provide a more productive understanding of the whole.

If *My Big TOE* communicates something of significance to you by resonating with your unique knowing, then this particular expression of the nature of reality suits your being. If it leaves you untouched, perhaps some other view of reality will speak to you more effectively. The form your understanding takes is not significant – it is the results that count! If you are prodded to a more productive understanding, you are on the right track. The expression of reality that most effectively nudges your understanding in the direction of learning, growing, and evolving a higher quality of being, is the right one for you. *My Big TOE* is not the only useful expression that Big Truth can take. Nevertheless, it is a uniquely comprehensive model of reality that speaks the language of the Western analytical approach. This Big TOE trilogy fully integrates a subjective, personal, and holistic worldview with objective science. East and West merge, not simply as a compatible or mutually reinforcing mixture, but as a fully integrated single solution.

When some people hear the word "model," they imagine a scale model – a miniature version of the real thing. *My Big TOE* has nothing to do with scale models. A model is an intellectual device that theoreticians use to achieve a more concrete understanding of an abstract concept. Models are often developed to describe an unknown function, interaction, or process (something that lies beyond our current individual experience) in terms of something more comprehensible. The model itself may closely resemble the reality it describes or merely describe its inputs and outputs. In either case, **do not confuse the model of reality with reality itself.** Please repeat that twice before going on.

If you have enough direct experience and a deep understanding of what is being modeled, the model becomes superfluous. With no direct experience, the model enables an understanding that is otherwise impossible to attain. With limited direct experience, the model allows you to place your limited experience within the context of the consistent logical structure of the model. To those with enough experience to incite curiosity and formulate practical questions, the model brings a meaningful interpretation and explanation to data (experience, information, fragments of truth) that otherwise seem hopelessly random and unconnected.

The model of reality developed within this trilogy enables you to understand the properties and characteristics of reality, how you interact with reality, the point of reality, and the boundaries, processes, functions, and mechanics of reality. It describes the what, the why and the how (the nature, purpose, and rules) of the interplay and interaction among sub-stance, energy, and consciousness. You will discover the distinction between the objective physical outside world and the subjective nonphys-ical inside world of mind and consciousness is wholly dependent upon, and relative to, the observer.

My Big TOE describes, as any Big TOE must, the basic oneness, conti-nuity, and connectedness of All That Is. It systematically and logically derives the natural relationships between mind and matter, physics and metaphysics, love and fear, and demonstrates how time, space, and con-sciousness are interconnected – all with a bare minimum of assumptions. Additionally, it describes in detail the most important processes of our reality – how and why reality works. You will find the results of *My Big TOE* to be in consonance with current data – and that it solves a host of longstanding scientific, philosophical, and metaphysical problems.

The model of reality developed within *My Big TOE* is not the only valid metaphor or description of the nature of the larger reality. Nevertheless, this model is perhaps more understandable to those of us who are accus-tomed to understanding our local reality in terms of the processes and measurements of objective causality. A materialistic or scientific defini-tion of reality is sometimes referred to as "Western" because the notion that reality is built upon an inviolate objective causality lies at the core of the Western cultural belief system.

My Big TOE is written to be especially accessible to this Western mind-set or Western attitude. The West does not now have, nor has it ever had, a monopoly on a process oriented, materialistic, and objective approach to existence and reality. We in the West have perhaps pursued science and technology more religiously than others, and have no doubt added a unique cultural slant to our particular brand of consumer-based materi-alism, but the basics of what I am calling a Western attitude are thor-oughly entrenched worldwide and expanding in every direction.

The stunning success of science and engineering in the twentieth cen-tury would seem to prove the usefulness as well as the correctness of this Western view. The result is that many people, whether from the East, West, North, or South of our planet, view reality from an objective and materialistic perspective that often coexists with some culturally based tra-ditional form of religious and social dogma.

Thus, a balance, or standoff, between our inner and outer needs evolves into a practical worldview that encourages Western material pro-ductivity. A pragmatic materialism that depends on objective causality is used to generate the appearance of a manipulatable, rational, stability on the outside, while a belief-system of some sort provides the necessary personal security on the inside. To eliminate the discomfort of conflicting worldviews, the two ends of this bipolar conceptual dichotomy are typically kept separate and do not mix or integrate to any significant depth. Each supports the other superficially as they together produce a materially focused, responsible, upwardly striving worker with a good work ethic, cooperative values, an inclination toward dependency, and a high tolerance of pain.

Because the Western mind-set is growing and spreading rapidly, and because the human spirit often withers on the vine before beginning to ripen in such an environment, it is particularly important to blaze a trail to the understanding of the larger reality in the terms, language, and metaphors of this mind-set. As a product of American culture myself, and as a scientist, I have endeavored to craft a model of the larger reality that not only appears rational to the objective Western attitude, but also provides a comprehensive, complete, and accurate model that Western science can build upon.

My Big TOE provides an understanding of reality that can profitably be used by both science and philosophy – one that provides an original perspective, and makes a significant contribution to physics and metaphysics as well as to several other traditional academic and practical disciplines. By the time you have finished Section 6, you will have been exposed not only to Big Picture physics and Big Picture metaphysics, but also to Big Picture psychology, biology, evolution, philosophy, computer science, artificial intelligence, and philosophy of science. There is even a TOE-bone to toss to the mathematicians – they will find new fractal concepts, and discover why geometric fractals successfully reproduce the likeness of natural objects. You will learn why Albert Einstein and others were unable to successfully develop Unified Field Theory, and why contemporary attempts to produce a successful TOE have been likewise frustrated.

The problem physicists are currently having describing a consistent reality is primarily because of the way they define space, time, objectivity, and consciousness. Their current ideas of these basic concepts contain limitations derived from erroneous cultural beliefs. It is this belief-induced blindness that creates scientific paradoxes (such as wave/particle duality and the instantaneous communication between an entangled pair). As Einstein pointed out more than half a century ago, space and time, as we interact with and experience them, are illusions. Many of the best scientists of the twentieth and twenty-first centuries realize this fact, but did not and do not know what to do about it or how to proceed. Their problem is one of perspective – their conceptualization of reality is too limited (only a little picture) to contain the answer.

Albert Einstein's space-time field (as described in his Unified Field Theory) asserted a nonphysical field as the basis for matter specifically and reality in general, thereby moving science closer to the truth, but he did not appreciate the discrete digital properties of space and time or the role of consciousness (instead of space-time) as the primary energy field. Einstein's student and colleague, the great quantum physicist David Bohm (along with a few of the best Quantum Mechanics theorists including Niels Bohr, Werner Heisenberg, and Eugene Vigner) made the consciousness connection but missed the digital connection and the Big Picture.

Contemporary physicist Edward Fredkin and his Digital Physics movement make the digital connection (quantized space and time) and are heading in the right direction, as was Einstein, Bohr, and Bohm, but they are missing a solid connection to consciousness. Digital physics has not yet discovered that consciousness **is** the computer. All are missing an appreciation of the natural limitations of our physical objective causality and a coherent vision of the Big Picture that ties everything together. You will be shown not only all of the pieces of this both ancient and contemporary reality-puzzle, but will also see how they fit together – philosophy and science, mind and matter, normal and paranormal – into a single unified coherent Big Picture.

You will hear more from the above-mentioned gentlemen of science, as well as many of the top Western thinkers of all time, in Section 6 where I integrate the concepts of *My Big TOE* with the knowledge base of traditional Western science and philosophy.

My Big TOE represents a scientific and logical tour of reality that goes considerably beyond the point where Einstein and other top scientists gave up in frustration. As limitations are removed from your thinking, you will see the source of their frustration clearly, how and why they got stuck, and the solution that they could not find or understand. That this is a non-technical exposition, devoid of the mathematical language of our little picture science, is actually not a weakness at all – even from a strict scientific perspective. How could that be? As you progress through *My Big TOE*, you will come to understand the **natural**, fundamental, and unavoidable limitations of little picture logic, science, and mathematics.

I will show you how physics is related to, and derived from, metaphysics. Additionally, you will find that mind, consciousness, and the paranormal are given a sound scientific explanation that stands upon a solid theoretical foundation. Not necessarily in the way hoped for and expected by traditional science – however, as you will discover, being nontraditional is a necessary strength, not an unavoidable weakness.

Sooner or later, truth must succeed and falsity must self-destruct. Although the consensus of culturally empowered opinion may carry the day, measurable results will carry the day after that. The value and success of *My Big TOE* must be based solely upon the personal and objective results that it produces. Only truth can produce significant consistent results. In contrast, falsity excels at producing assertive beliefs, arguments, and opinions. Open your mind, remain skeptical, pursue only significant measurable results, and let the chips fall where they may.

My Big TOE is in the form of a reality model at a level that is necessarily unusual, but easy to understand. It provides an exploration of the scientific and philosophical implications of consciousness evolution, a subject that holds critical significance for everyone.

Because this material must develop entirely new scientific and reality paradigms, it requires an extensive presentation to shed light upon the limitations of culturally habituated patterns of thought – a goal that cannot be both quickly and effectively reached. Such an in-depth multi-disciplined analysis is better suited to a trilogy than to the condensed formal structure of a traditional scientific paper.

The focus of this trilogy is directed toward the potential significance that *My Big TOE* holds for each individual reader. These books were written for you – you will find their tone to be more personal than general, more of a sharing of experience and concepts, than a lecture by an expert. It is your potential personal interaction with this material that has initiated, as well as driven, its development.

You will find an open, logical, and skeptical mind with a broad depth of experience is much more helpful than a technical background. The details of little picture reality are by nature highly technical, the exclusive territory of modern science and mathematics. On the other hand, Big Picture reality is available and accessible to **anyone** with an open mind and the will to apply it. There are no requirements for formal education or technical credentials in order to understand what is presented here.

There are three main challenges that must be met in order to deliver a shrink-wrapped Big TOE to the general public. First, with shirtsleeves rolled up and the lights turned on, I must turn some portion of metaphysics into physics because I intend to describe the whole of reality – mind and matter, normal and paranormal – not merely the matter and normal part. Consequently, metaphysics is where I must start – our contemporary physics will naturally flow from the metaphysics. The second challenge is to package this unavoidably far-out subject in a way that is interesting, easily readable, intellectually engaging, and non-threatening. To this end, I use the format of a one-on-one, peer-to-peer, informal discussion between the reader and me. The third challenge is to make and keep *My Big TOE* credible – to stay tightly logical while straightforwardly explaining the data of our collective and individual experience.

Culturally conditioned mental reflexes may need to be re-examined, generalized, and expanded. The fact that some of the content of this trilogy is likely to lie far beyond the comfortable familiarity of your personal experience creates a difficult communications problem for both of us. *My Big TOE* not only requires you to think out-of-the-box, but out-of-the-ballpark (if not out-of-the-universe), as well. You will be challenged to overcome deep seated knee-jerk cultural drag in order to climb high enough up the mountain to get a good view.

Modern science and technology are only now providing the combined knowledge by which metaphysics can be understood. It should not be too surprising that science, in its relentless explorations of the unknown, would one day arrive at the roots of existence itself. As it turns out, the nature of reality has both an objective and a subjective component. *My Big TOE* provides a thoroughly scientific description of an objective Theory Of Everything that covers all aspects of reality in an entirely general way. Additionally, it provides a remarkably practical, personally significant understanding of subjective consciousness, and explains how you individually are related to the larger reality. To appreciate and deeply understand the personal or subjective nature of consciousness, you must grow your own Big TOE. One of the major goals of *My Big TOE* is to provide the logical conceptual framework, materials, tools, and direction that you need to independently grow your Big TOE.

My Big TOE will provide the foundation and structure that you need to make sense of both your objective and subjective experience. Your personal Big Understanding of Big Truth must flow primarily from **your** direct experience – not from your intellect alone. This trilogy will bring your objective and subjective experience together under one coherent understanding of the whole you.

Please understand, I did **not** put the "My" in *My Big TOE* to flaunt pride of authorship. Nor does the "My" indicate any lack of generality or applicability to others. The "My" was added to be a constant reminder to you that this reality model cannot serve as your **personal** Big TOE until it is based upon your **personal** experience. On the other hand, personal or subjective experience is only one piece of the reality puzzle. In the objective physical world of traditional science, *My Big TOE* delivers a comprehensive model of reality that subsumes modern science, describes our objective material reality, and is universally applicable. Contemporary physics is shown to be a special case of a more general set of basic principles. After reading the *My Big TOE* trilogy, you will better understand the universal (objective) and the personal (subjective) nature of perception, consciousness, reality, and Big TOEs. You will learn to appreciate the fact that the larger reality extends beyond objective causality, beyond the reach of intellectual effort, into the subjective mind of each individual. **My** *Big TOE* is the launch pad. **Your** Big TOE is the final destination.

A personal Big TOE is necessary because the larger reality, like your consciousness, has a subjective component as well as a collective objective component. The larger reality cannot be fully appreciated or understood merely by studying, or reading about it. You must experience it. Additionally, your understanding of the Big Picture must be sufficient to integrate your subjective experience with your shared objective knowledge or both will remain superficial. To the traditional scientist and other left-brained analytical types, what I have just said sounds suspiciously like a mixing of real science and hocus-pocus, touchy-feely, belief-baloney. It is not, but a properly skeptical mind may need to digest all three books before that becomes apparent.

Arriving at conclusions based upon the assumed infallibility and apparent truth of culturally, personally, and professionally embedded paradigms and dogmas will make it difficult to understand the larger reality. Change and new ways of thinking are often traumatic, difficult to integrate, and generally unwelcome. Resistance to change is automatic at the gut level; we cling to familiar ways for the security and comfort they provide. We do not easily see unfamiliar patterns. You must be willing to overcome fear and rise above self-imposed belief-blindness if you are to succeed in getting a good look at the Big Picture.

In the pages ahead, we are going to explore the reality-wilderness. This trilogy is about the how, what, and why of what is. It is about physics and metaphysics, your world and other worlds. It is about beginnings, endings, mind and matter, point and purpose – it is also about the quality of your personal consciousness.

Your intellectual understanding of the reality you exist within, and are a part of, is only the beginning – a place to start. The most important action, the real fun, begins **after** you have finished the trilogy and begin to apply what you have learned about reality and the Big Picture to the rest of your life – both professionally and personally.

Though you will soon learn there is more to reality than theory and facts, here is one fact that you should consider before you begin: Big Truth, once understood and assimilated, always modifies your intent, and invariably leads to personal change.

■■■
List of Acronyms, Symbols, and Foreign Words and Phrases Used Within Book 3
■■■

Acronym	Descriptive Name	Page (First Mention)
AUM	Absolute Unbounded Manifold	41
AUO	Absolute Unbounded Oneness	41
Big TOE	Big Picture Theory Of Everything	9
CEO	Chief Executive Officer	114
EBC	Even Bigger Computer	41
NPMR	Nonphysical-Matter Reality	41
OOBE	Out Of Body Experience	142
OS	Our System	41
PMR	Physical-Matter Reality	41
RWW	Reality Wide Web	67
TBC	The Big Computer	41
TOE	Theory Of Everything	9

Foreign Words and Phrases:

gedanken experiment – thought experiment; a logical experiment performed only in the mind.

über alles – over all; over and above all else.

Que será, será – whatever will be will be

Synopsis of Book 1 and Book 2

Book 1: *Awakening* **– Section 1** provides a partial biography of the author that is pertinent to the subsequent creation of this trilogy. This brief look at the author's unique experience and credentials sheds some light upon the origins of this extraordinary work. The unusual associations, circumstances, training, and research that eventually led to the creation of the *My Big Picture Theory Of Everything* (My Big TOE) trilogy are described to provide a more accurate perspective of the whole.

Book 1: *Awakening* **– Section 2** lays out, logically justifies, and defines the basic conceptual building blocks needed to construct *My Big TOE's* conceptual foundation. It discusses the cultural beliefs that trap our thinking into a narrow and limited conceptualization of reality, defines the basics of Big Picture epistemology and ontology, as well as examines the nature and practice of meditation. Most importantly, Section 2 defines and develops the two fundamental assumptions upon which this trilogy is based – a high entropy primordial consciousness energy-form called AUO (Absolute Unbounded Oneness) and the Fundamental Process of evolution. AUO eventually evolves to become a much lower-entropy consciousness energy-form called AUM (Absolute Unbounded Manifold) though neither is absolute or unbounded. Using only these two assumptions, Section 2 logically infers the nature of time, space, and consciousness as well as describes the basic properties, purpose, and mechanics of our reality. Additionally, Section 2 develops the concepts of The Big Computer (TBC) and the Even Bigger Computer (EBC) as operational models of aware digital consciousness. Our System (OS) is defined to be PMR (Physical Matter Reality – our physical universe) **plus** the subset of NPMRN [A specific part of Nonphysical Matter Reality (NPMR)] that is interactive with PMR. Many of the concepts initiated in Section 2 are more fully explained in later Sections.

Book 2: *Discovery* **– Section 3** develops the interface and interaction between we the people and our digital consciousness reality. It derives and explains the characteristics, origins, dynamics, and function of ego, love, free will, and our larger purpose. This section introduces us to the consciousness-evolution fractal ecosystem of which we are a part and explains how we can optimize our interaction within that system to actualize our full potential as an individuated consciousness. Additionally, Section 3 builds a bridge between your present assumptions about the physical and spiritual reality you think you live in (a reality limited by your cultural and personal beliefs) and My Big Picture Theory Of Everything (*My Big TOE*). The nature of a larger reality that exists beyond your physical perception is described in detail. Spirituality and Love are technically defined as functions of entropy content within consciousness. Paranormal activity is given a theoretical basis as a normal part of a larger science. Finally, Section 3 develops the psi uncertainty principle as it explains and interrelates psi phenomena, free will, love, consciousness evolution, physics, reality, human purpose, digital computation, and entropy.

Book 2: *Discovery* **– Section 4** describes an operational and functional model of consciousness that further develops the results of Section 3 and supports the conclusions of Section 5. The origins and nature of digital consciousness are described along with how artificial intelligence (AI), as embodied in AI Guy, leads to artificial consciousness, which leads to actual consciousness and to us. The design criteria, features, and limitations of our personal consciousness are explained and related to the larger digital reality. The part we play within the whole is derived as the physical universe is shown to be a local reality within a larger multidimensional system of digital synergy. The concepts of physical and nonphysical are shown to be relative to the observer and to carry no intrinsic significance of their own. Section 4 derives our physical universe, our science, and our perception of a physical reality. The mind-matter dichotomy is solved as both our physical reality and the larger reality are directly derived from a large but finite system of digital energy that evolves an organized content called consciousness.

Section 5

■ ■ ■

Inner Space, the Final Frontier: The Mechanics of Nonphysical Reality – A Model

---

■ ■ ■

1

■ ■ ■

Introduction to Section 5

■ ■ ■

In Sections 2, 3, and 4, I have developed the basic concepts needed to gain a fundamental understanding of the larger reality. In this section those concepts serve as the necessary background required to produce a top-level understanding of PMR-NPMR interface dynamics. You will have to make most of the connections between the earlier sections and this section on your own. If I were to point out all the places where concepts of previous sections are being applied, it would add so many references to Section 5 you would have difficulty staying focused.

In Section 5 we will regress to a more PMR-centric view that should be more familiar and less abstract, develop a description of OS reality mechanics, and afterward explore some of its more interesting ramifications. This section will begin by reviewing from a more analytic perspective some of what we have previously learned. This conceptual review will set the stage for a challenging exposition of the fundamental processes of the larger reality.

Section 5 will be a little more buttoned down and logically formal, a little more technical and precise, but don't let that put you off; after the heavy brain work is done formulating the fundamentals of NPMR mechanics, we will have some fun exploring some of the cooler ramifications.

The following twelve chapters, which deliver the content of Section 5, are a subset of my observations relevant to describing the mechanics of the larger reality in which we all exist. They are carefully constructed from my experience in physical-matter reality (PMR) and nonphysical-matter reality (NPMR). This is a broad brush across the top of this subject, a first pass so that you can tell if you want to dig deeper on your own. Many interesting and important concepts are purposely neglected because they fall beyond the scope of this effort to present a comprehensive model of how the larger reality works. With a subject as broad as this one (the mechanics of reality), I have no choice but to remain focused so that you are not overwhelmed with endless digressions nor a work that is too ponderous to ponder.

Please keep in mind that the point of developing a consistent Big Picture model of reality is **not** to convince or persuade you of the correctness of **my** interpretation of **my** experience, and thereby offer you something better or more accurate to believe concerning the nature of reality. After many years of careful exploration, I have merely organized my observations into a coherent and consistent pattern – the resulting structure is the Big TOE reality model presented in this section.

My intent is that the overall model of reality described by the *MY Big TOE* trilogy should be a model that you can apply; it should be practical as well as theoretical. Its primary usefulness lies in its ability to help you meet and solve some of your most daunting professional and personal challenges. Second, it provides a logical unified theoretical understanding of the reality of which you are a part. If you are a scientist or philosopher, it is this secondary usefulness that will seem most important – it is not. You will, most likely, depart the *MY Big TOE* experience with something that was not there before, something that reflects your personal experience, understanding, and quality. Take from it whatever you can. Leave behind whatever does not square with your sense of what is right. Have no fear; you will not end up where you do not belong.

The first four relatively short chapters of this book will provide a quick review and wrap-up of the concepts developed in the first two books of this trilogy, as well as provide the proper perspective that you will need to optimize your understanding of the reality model presented in Chapters 5 through 10. This review is primarily intended for those that have not yet read Book 1 or Book 2. If you have recently read the first two books you may wish to skim the next three chapters spending time only on those concepts that are of particular interest to you.

Chapters 5 through 10 are more conceptually challenging: If you get stuck simply continue to skip paragraphs until it gets easier (or more interesting) again.

Book 3 not only presents the Mechanics of Reality, but also explores and describes some of its consequences. In the process of doing so, it touches on fun subjects including time travel, teleportation and telepathy; the simultaneity of past, present, and future; how the past continues to live; changing the past; warp drives (faster than light travel or communications); the concept of an Even Bigger Computer (EBC); the nature of NPMR and its beings; probable realities, precognition, and future expectations; changing the probability of occurrence of future events; multiple projections of you; leaving the PMR body behind; creating multiple bodies; understanding reality as a Consciousness-Evolution fractal; and many other interesting subjects.

2

■ ■ ■

Science, Truth, Knowledge, Reality, and You

■ ■ ■

My *Big TOE* describes a model – a relational logical structure – that defines the forms, functions, and processes that constitute your larger reality. The approach is scientific (I use the word "science" in its original and most general sense: The observation, identification, description, experimental investigation, and theoretical explanation of phenomena). The observations have been accumulated and the investigations undertaken by the author during the past thirty years. It is experience, not faith, which is required to transform the information found here into knowledge, and to evaluate its significance to you. You must find your own meaning in it.

If what you find here does not resonate with your inner knowledge, or if it only resonates with anger or other negative feelings, let it go. Toss the book out and forget about it. It is not our time to connect. Learning cannot and should not be forced. Each individual must grow in his own way, on his own path, under his own power and initiative. The world is big enough for everyone if mutual respect is given to personal differences.

In as much as being careful, vigilant, and practicing good science can make it possible, this effort is based entirely on my direct firsthand **experience** – it is not based on my beliefs or on what I may have surmised from others. The influence of philosophical bias, preconceived notions, or beliefs has been, to the best of my ability, eliminated or at least minimized. The data upon which this model is based represent my best **objective** evaluation of my **subjective** experience.

If you think the previous sentence contains an oxymoron (that an objective evaluation of subjective experience is impossible), you probably have too narrow a definition of the word "objective" and may be muddling through the most important parts of your life ignoring objective feedback that is the **result** of subjective interpretation of apparently objective perceptions. Results can be objectively measured even if the motivations, understanding, and intent (the underlying dynamics) that created those results are entirely subjective. Unique, stable, repeatable, recognizable subjective states often drive specific objective results: This is the normal mode of operation for most individuals.

Consider some of the correct, objective conclusions or knowledge (truth) you have come to, or gained, from your subjectively driven and interpreted interactions with friends, family members, lovers, spouses, children, bosses, or parents and from the subjective evaluation of the direction, substance, and quality of your life. Consider that useful logical conclusions may flow from inductive as well as deductive reasoning. If you are still in a logical dilemma about the possibility of deriving truth (objective knowledge) from subjective experience, reread Chapter 13, Book 2 before going on. Further explanation of how subjective experience can produce objective results is presented in the next chapter.

This trilogy, as with all sincere science, has universal truth as its goal – a goal that is, unfortunately, always difficult, if not impossible, to **guarantee**. The correctness of this model, as with all scientific models (the shell model of the atom, for example), must be judged by its ability to explain the existing data within a self-consistent and coherent system. If you are not sure how that might be accomplished (evaluating the correctness of this model), it might be a good idea to reread Chapter 14, Book 2.

The nature of the existing data that describes the facts of reality is unique enough to require some further discussion. It is a common mistake to confuse the larger reality itself with the objects that appear to lie within it. We shall see that this error produces a limiting view that extends only as far as our senses. It also denies the reality and significance of what is most important to us. The super-set of facts, truths, or data describing our larger reality must include who and what we are (our subjective being, our mind, our consciousness), what we perceive through our physical senses (our objective measurements), and the result of interpreting, integrating and synthesizing this data into the unique intellectual, emotional, physical, and spiritual being we call us.

Unlike traditional works in either philosophy or science, I make no effort to convince the reader of the goodness-of-fit of this model to the existing data; that is not the point. I know this is difficult to understand because it is contrary to how things are normally done: You will need to think out of the box here. Although I am formally presenting a scientific Theory of Everything with this trilogy, **convincing you** that my concepts are correct or credible, or that the model is accurate or valuable, is not at all what these books are about. Understanding the content, knowing its truth (and the limitations and boundaries of its truth) at a deep and personal level, must be personally earned, not book-learned; it must come through your first hand experience, not through reading (and being convinced) about results and conclusions based on someone else's experience.

What is the point? In addition to offering you a coherent understanding of reality and time, explaining the purpose and significance of your existence, and describing how your world works, this model, in conjunction with your effort, may help you interpret both your objective and subjective reality data (experience). Perhaps it will nudge you to create some interesting theories of your own; or, by providing some missing pieces of understanding or information, it may help you find explanations to a personal puzzle within your experience. Additionally, it might be a catalyst to your learning by expanding the set of possibilities of which you are aware. It may lead, nudge or goad you to think new thoughts, to evaluate important perspectives, concepts and ideas that you otherwise wouldn't have considered.

My Big TOE in general or this "mechanics of reality" section in particular is **not** likely to **create** significant knowledge at a deep or fundamental level where none existed before. Contemplating this book (or any book) is unlikely to change who you are or the quality of your being and yet at the same time, and most importantly, there is an outside chance it could be the catalyst for **you** to do exactly that.

The personal nature of at least a portion of the data (the facts of reality) makes the standard argumentative (me convincing you) approach to imparting knowledge counterproductive – this approach would guarantee a failed effort. It would succeed only in starting a non-solvable argument over what constitutes the set of valid existing data. A useless and endless argument for sure. Why? Because what qualifies as the existing data is both objective and subjective and the subjective portion is unique and personal to each individual's experience and knowledge (recall Chapters 14, 32, and 33 of Book 2). Your consciousness is personal to you, it represents your being – we will call it, its attributes and evolutionary processes "being objects." In contrast, consider your body or other physical objects can that be probed, measured, and tabulated by the intellect and tools of others; we will call these objects shared "intellectual objects."

A set of the data relevant to the larger reality must take into account your consciousness as well as your body. Intellectual objects are physical objects, shared public objects, objects that must obey the objective causality (space-time rule-set) of PMR. Being objects are nonphysical and primarily represented by units of individuated consciousness in various states of awareness and quality.

A system capable of supporting consciousness spontaneously generates enough self-organizing potential so that the Fundamental Process of evolution can, in the pursuit of profitability, generate sufficient synergy (through a process of recursive reorganization called learning) to form an individuated consciousness that is independent of the mechanisms that support it. Consider a digital system's potential to profitably organize itself as constituting a nonphysical form of energy such that the system itself becomes an energetic media that the Fundamental Process can organize and reorganize into successively lower entropy configurations. Being objects are the individual result of the consciousness creation process. (Chapters 7 and 23 of Book 2 review these concepts.)

Reality must be experienced by consciousness. Unlike the intellectual objects (material facts, and ideas) of traditional Western science that can be shared, being objects or unique states of being are primarily experienced through subjective personal awareness. To understand the knowledge, data, and facts of being (the being objects), you must be them – you must reflect, express, or integrate them in your being.

So, what is the point of *My Big TOE* intellectually discussing being objects? Because knowing about it, though not to be confused with being it, can be valuable in and of itself. Consider the difference between wisdom and knowledge. Knowledge is generally good to have and it is required in order to apply wisdom, but wisdom is much more than merely better, or more complete, knowledge. Have you ever heard of a little wisdom being a dangerous thing? In addition to knowledge, wisdom requires Big Picture understanding and caring at a deep level – both are attributes of experience and being rather than attributes of information. With the right information you might occasionally act wisely, but that is not at all the same as being wise.

Experience, not verbal communication, is the doorway through which personal subjective knowing must pass. One who is successful at acquiring, assimilating, and manipulating intellectual objects is said to be knowledgeable and is capable of **doing** great **things** (has good quality ideas). In contrast, one who has successfully evolved low entropy being objects is said to be wise and capable of **being** a great **person** (has good spiritual quality). Each of us should develop both of these mutually reinforcing capacities and seek an optimal balance between them.

Knowledge without wisdom is common; wisdom without knowledge is impossible. Knowledge is about facts; wisdom understands how those facts relate and interact within the Big Picture. Intellectual objects are separable and can be arranged like beads on a thread. Being objects are individualized subsets of one whole integrated thing – more like the thread itself.

Unfortunately, learning to manipulate intellectual or material objects is seen as real, rational, and scientific (the scientific method is used to separate fact from fiction among intellectual objects) while learning to manipulate being objects is seen as non-real (delusional), irrational, and unscientific. Just as classical mechanics makes hopelessly wrong inferences in the realms of the very small and very fast, the scientific method has little validity outside its realm of intellectual objects.

The scientific method we learned to venerate for its proven ability to deliver the truth is an excellent methodology for exploring Newton's mechanistic universe as well as Einstein's relative universe. However, a digital (quantized) statistical reality (somewhat like the one described by quantum mechanics), based upon the constraints of our knowing, needs a broader scientific methodology that allows for the necessity of uncertainty. Such a generalized scientific method will allow a larger more porous truth to be derived from uncertain statistical data manipulated by inductive as well as deductive reasoning.

Living with uncertainty is fundamental to your progress and growth. It is the way of the future, scientifically and personally, and you might as well get used to it. A mechanistic reality over which we eventually learn (through science) to exert control represents a limited local reality. Uncertainty is not a problem for science as long as the uncertain results are represented in our physical reality by something (a physical component or manifestation) that is clearly measurable, consistent, and uniquely related to its source.

To apply the requirements of the current science of intellectual and material **objects** to the science of being is to deny the existence of the latter. Turning the scientific method into a universal dogma (science as religion) enforces an inappropriate process and measure of value upon the science of being. By the standards of traditional science, the science of being will (by definition) always seem delusional, non-provable and unusable – the realm of charlatans, kooks, and other silly or devious people.

People in general (Western science and philosophy in particular) are ill-equipped and ill-prepared to crack the nut of mind, being, psi (paranormal phenomena), love, or of spirituality. Nor are they likely to understand how these things interconnect with each other, the physical world, and us (collectively and individually). Not until individuals, particularly scientists, learn to transcend (think outside the box) the philosophical corner they have dogmatically painted themselves into will the science of consciousness become available for our use.

For these reasons, I will leave the analysis of the model's goodness of fit to existing data and previously acquired knowledge up to those who have enough honest (not generated from fear, dogma, or belief) experiential data points to make the exercise meaningful. The model's value for those without first hand experience of the larger reality lies in its ability to provide a comprehensive theoretical model of existence, and in providing a tool that can be used to logically extend one's experience beyond present knowledge.

The exploration of inner space is greatly facilitated by the encouragement and assurances of those who have gone before, and by having a good map and description of the territory.

The value of *My Big TOE* is entirely dependent on the essential correctness of its representation. You should gather up your objective (public) experience and integrate it with your objectively evaluated **subjective** (private) experience to assess this TOE's value for yourself. You could evaluate only the public part, but that would be like inventing an automobile and only using it to crack walnuts by driving back and forth over them one at a time. Surely, you **can** use a car as a nutcracker, but why would you want to do that? Wouldn't you rather use your car to go somewhere interesting – to explore the Big Picture perhaps? Cracking those walnuts is simply not that important. Lift up your head and look around – there is an entire reality out there – let the nuts go for a while.

For each individual sentient being, life's most important and meaningful experiences are typically subjective. Significance, relative to the being objects, or relative to the quality of an individual's being, is derived primarily from subjective experience. Consequently, it is important to keep the following two things in mind – **both apply to you, as well as to me**: 1) The ignorant are never aware of their ignorance; and 2) It is highly likely there are individuals who possess more experience, understanding, wisdom and truth than you do. How can you discover which individuals know more, and are more, than what you know and what you are (represent a higher quality of being, contain less entropy, or are more spiritually evolved)? Likewise, how can you discover which ones know less, and are less, than what you know and what you are?

Given that you do not believe yourself to be omniscient (a typically ego or fear driven know-it-all), you can only attempt to sort out the resultant confusion (separating the wise from the foolish) by gaining **direct**, carefully sorted, tested, and validated firsthand experience. Experience is the key because of the personal nature of the subject – you must personally experience the larger reality – there is no other way to interact or to absorb it. Nevertheless, if you are not careful how you evaluate and interpret your subjective experience, you could still end up in the self-delusional fool category. If instead, you separate the wise from the foolish by applying your beliefs, you logically risk being merely a self-consistent fool – or one fool among many (an invisible fool) if your beliefs are shared by others.

Separating the wise from the foolish is no easy task, but it is one at which you can succeed if you try. Recall that in Chapter 14, Book 2 we offered a detailed solution to this epistemological dilemma.

In the science of being, unlike the science of objects, consensus does not define the accepted truth, much less the actual truth. Experience is personal and can never be shared exactly – an event or happening can be shared (simultaneously viewed) by many individuals, but the experience of it is unique to each individual. Consequently, there are many ways an individual can view (and interact with) the same truth. What you do with the truth you discover is the point; how will you use it to enhance the quality of your being? Functionality (what can be done with it) and results (how it actually helps you grow or evolve your consciousness quality) are the measures of the value of your knowledge, not how many people agree with you. Big Truth does not rearrange itself to fit the whims or demands of the fashionable majority.

My experience, knowledge, and understanding are important to you only if they help you find knowledge, and experience truth in **your own** way. Your and my understanding of the right way, and of how things work, may or may not be helpful to others. If we think that our experience and the knowledge derived therefrom might be helpful, we should share it, but never impose it, require it, or think it is the critical information that others need. Nor should we make it our goal to ensure that others recognize its universality – that is evangelism, not science.

The science of being is an individual science that cannot be advanced through a group effort. Its significance lies in its results – in the effect it has on the quality of the individual and on that individual's ability and willingness to profitably evolve his or her personal consciousness. As you read this section, focus on the common understanding, not the differences, between this model and other concepts of reality. Reach for the biggest picture your personal data can logically support, but be careful to avoid imitating the proverbial blind men who jump to conclusions about the characteristics of an elephant from the one part of the whole that they experience.

Keep in mind that our (yours and mine) experience is probably incomplete. Conclusions should remain flexible, tentative, be given varying degrees of credibility based upon **our** experience, and remain always open to the possibility of gaining more data (understanding) in the future.

Either believing or disbelieving what you read here would be a futile act, a compulsion that cannot induce personal growth. My aim is to expand the possibilities that inhabit your mind, to provide you with a model that helps you place your experience into a larger context, and that encourages you, by explaining the scope, structure, and content of a larger reality, to explore and find truth. I hope that you will find freedom and empowerment in the idea that you create (as well as limit) your own reality and find comfort in the vastness of the possibilities and potential that you have to satisfy the fundamental purpose of your being.

Let me be clear that *My Big TOE* in general, or the mechanics of reality presented in this section in particular, do **not** philosophically center about Western science, Eastern religion, spiritualism, new age philosophy, theosophy, the occult, or any other body of thought or "ism." It is simply my experience put in the context of form, function and process. Though *My Big TOE* may logically connect, and occasionally overlap, with many philosophical, scientific, and theological traditions, it represents and has been derived from a unique synthesis of my personal and professional experience. Big Truth is, and has always been, the same as it is now, so similarities should be expected.

Any associations you might draw connecting the concepts presented in this trilogy to some other body of thought or to another set of concepts are a synthesis of your own brewing, not the specific intention of the author. Make connections – that is good. Intellectual synthesis is necessary, helpful and important, but **your** connections are much more significant than any that I might point out to you.

Open minded skepticism is the correct frame of mind with which to proceed through this section – anything else may lead you astray. Do not be predisposed to confirm or deny what you read, or you will likely miss some important points and have a less than optimal learning opportunity.

3

■■■

Preliminaries

■■■

Though we have previously used the terms PMR and NPMR in a general
way in previous sections, now we need to become more precise.

PMR (Physical-Matter Reality) – The reality that your body lives in,
and its properties, and laws (physics). PMR includes the material universe,
galaxies, solar systems, planets, and everything known and unknown that
materially exists within them. PMR can be effectively and purposefully
manipulated (is operationally viable) and is inhabited by beings that are
sentient in it.

NPMR (Nonphysical-matter Reality) – Everything other than PMR.
The non-material (from the view of PMR) superset of PMR that contains
its own unique properties, materials, and laws. Like PMR, NPMR can also
be effectively and purposefully manipulated (is operationally viable) and
is inhabited by beings that are sentient in it.

NPMR contains unique dimensions, material, and time that consistently and necessarily follows its own rules (physics). It exists independently of PMR and may contain numerous unique local realities as subsets.

[If this definition logically trips you up, or seems insupportable, simply
continue. Admittedly, it is only an initial attempt to provide a narrow, purposely limited, PMR-centric working definition of NPMR. Its precision is
not fundamental to what follows – you will get a clearer sense for NPMR
as you progress through this section.]

These definitions of physical and nonphysical were chosen to serve the
largest group of people with a minimum of confusion. Both PMR and
NPMR are real physical places from the point of view of the consciousness beings that inhabit them. They each contain objects and sentient
beings that appear to have substance, form, structure, and energy that are

measurable and perceivable and follow the rules, causality, and science (physics) peculiar to their respective realms. The apparent difference between nonphysical and physical is relative to the observer. From within a given local reality (a specific dimension of AUM or TBC), everything within that reality appears physical while everything outside of that reality appears nonphysical.

Defining NPMR as nonphysical is a parochial PMR-centric view that implies our physical PMR science is fundamentally incapable of expanding its vision to include NPMR as a part of our physical reality. Simply moving beyond the limited idea that PMR defines all possible reality will open up new worlds of potential existence to exploration and study. Breakthroughs must always begin with the unthinkable.

Most people are comfortable with the fuzzy notion that what we can **directly measure** (with our five senses and their extensions by our marvelous machines of science) **in PMR** is by definition physical and everything else is nonphysical. This is sometimes called the operational definition of physical reality. This places two familiar groups of things into the nonphysical camp: those that are inferred but not yet **directly** measurable (neutrinos for example), and those that are conceptual (such as wave packets, dark matter, strings as in physics theory, as well as ego, love, ethics, and justice). Inferred entities can only be **indirectly** measured by actually measuring something else that is assumed to be causally related.

Conceptual things (such as justice or wave packets) are inferred. Initially, conceptual entities are defined into existence (as were neutrinos or quarks) by our need for them to support and maintain the consistency of our current worldview. Their operational functionality and their ability to help us maintain logical consistency is accepted as proof of their **potential** physical reality. We take them seriously because they help us define, understand, and control our local reality; they are operationally significant. That they are initially operationally nonphysical (cannot be directly measured) only relegates their existence to the theoretical, not to the absurd. They are in the wings waiting for scientific experience to give them full membership into the world of the physically measurable – or at least into the world of things with physically measurable effects. Thus it is with mind, consciousness, and intuition – all operationally significant, all with indirectly measurable effects.

Nonphysical does not mean non-useful, non-real, or non-existent. Nonphysical things are often defined by (are real and meaningful because of) their effective use, their application, their interaction with measurable things, and their ability to satisfy (fit, or be consistent with) the current overarching model from which their reality, existence, and meaningfulness is derived. They are directly inferred from basic assumptions about the nature of reality.

The beings, objects, and energy in NPMR are directly inferred in the same way. Anyone can easily learn to see unique and specific energy forms with the mind's eye, manipulate the energy of creation, and communicate telepathically with beings in NPMR or PMR. However, whether or not these activities can be considered real and meaningful depends upon their effective use, their application, their interaction with measurable things, and their ability to satisfy (fit, or be consistent with) an overarching model.

Overarching models of being are in short supply. Current efforts are typically incomplete or narrowly dogmatic. Ontology (the branch of metaphysics that deals with the nature of being) is not taken seriously by many philosophers or scientists because it is considered to be beyond objective discourse. They are half right: A comprehensive model of being like the one presented in the *My Big TOE* trilogy is beyond the causal logic of the little picture, but rather than decree that no logical objective solution can possibly exist, science and philosophy would be better served by open mindedly searching for a more general view that would broaden its understanding. Perhaps, with an open minded approach, scientists and philosophers could find a bigger picture that contains a logical solution that answers to a higher level (more general superset) of objective causality. Unfortunately, it is easier and more immediately rewarding to decree the impossibility of difficult to understand solutions, or posit belief-based pseudo-solutions, than to live with the nagging uncertainty that is required to find real solutions through better science.

We have been struggling to understand the Big Picture in Western culture for at least 2,700 years with only spotty success because our materialistically-based belief system blocks genuine progress. Big Picture models cannot be taken seriously in our Westernized techno-culture because of a pervasive little picture objectivity *über alles* delusion. The world, and particularly the Western world, desperately needs a Big TOE to provide balance and stability.

A living theory is one that embraces change and the possibility of new and contradictory knowledge, as opposed to being an impossible to change, know-it-all dead dogma. Big Picture models of being, reality, or existence must continually be in the process of evolving Big Truth. In the same sense, most physical models (modern physics theories) are also living. Dead models, if correct, must be small in scope. A model that is broad in application and far ranging in its consequences (large scope) must remain open to the idea of redefining itself periodically or risk degenerating into a belief-based old dogma that is incapable of learning new tricks. There is always more to learn. How can we claim completion when AUM is still learning and growing? Believing that your uncertain ignorance is small compared to your certain knowledge is the signature assumption of fools.

In the simplest sense, and at the most basic level of understanding, the nonphysical being objects in NPMR are important because they are significant and valuable to individuals. They consistently, powerfully, clearly, and **measurably** can, and do, contribute to your consciousness quality and the evolvement of your being. These nonphysical being objects and processes influence (interact with) your being whether you are aware of it or not. The advantage of being aware of the interface and interaction you have with NPMR is that this awareness can dramatically raise the efficiency of the experience-knowledge-growth transfer function.

The bottom line is that NPMR, just like neutrinos, is inferred from repeatable consistent results that are indirectly measurable in PMR by independent researchers. *My Big TOE* develops the notion of NPMR as part of an overarching consistent scientific theory of reality that includes PMR and its physics as a subset.

Though this section is purposely developed from a PMR-centric viewpoint to enhance comprehension at a more familiar level, hang onto your larger perspective and integrate what you find here with whatever constitutes your biggest picture. As we pointed out toward the end of Book 2, PMR and NPMR are dimensions or subsets of one reality as seen from differing points of view. The terms physical and nonphysical have no intrinsic meaning beyond describing a local belief-based delusional perception of other realities relative to one's own. There is **no** primary physical reality, just as there is **no** primary inertial frame in relativity theory. There is but one reality that can be viewed from many different perspectives. Same old story (relativity of perception) repeated at a higher level of generality.

▶ The definition of beings, objects and energy are the same in PMR and NPMR. In PMR, physical objects and energy form the set of all non-sentient things. Let's revisit the definition of sentient. The dictionary defines sentient as: "Having sense perception; conscious; experiencing sensation or feeling." I will again generalize this official PMR definition by saying that sentient entities are self-aware and aware of their environment. Additionally, sentient entities make deliberate choices that have significant consequences to themselves and perhaps to others. (Recall that the origins and evolution of self-awareness are discussed in detail in Chapter 25, Book 1.)

The upper echelons of sentient things are often called beings, though technically everything sentient is a being. In NPMR, objects and energy are defined in exactly the same way. Objects and energy within NPMR represent all the things in NPMR that are not sentient in NPMR. Thus, the phrase: "beings, objects, and energy" includes everything when applied to either PMR or NPMR. The beings are the choice makers, the objects includes all other things, and the energy state relative to a set of objects is neither a being nor an object but has the ability to effect changes in both.

Most of the significant (within the Big Picture) changes that occur between time increments within a given reality are driven by the interactive free will choices of the beings who inhabit that reality. Objects (such as rocks, mountains, clouds, thermal geysers, or rivers) and interactive forms of energy (storms, volcanic eruptions, or earth quakes, for example) are very predictable when one has **all** the data.

Beings, objects, and energy do, however, sometimes have random components associated with their choices. Some degree of randomness (usually relatively small) may influence what happens next. ◀

Our practical (from a PMR viewpoint) definition of physical and nonphysical reflects the common separation (particularly in the West) between mental and physical – mind and body – even though it is obvious to almost everyone that these two opposites are hopelessly entangled and integrated. PMR and NPMR are likewise entangled. The **directly** unmeasurable (within PMR) mind, consciousness, thought, and soul clearly fall into the nonphysical (from a PMR viewpoint) camp regardless of whether or not there is a presumed physical basis.

In summary, our operational definition of PMR causes some of the common things taken seriously (believed in and relied on) in physics – such as neutrinos, quarks, and string theory – to belong in the nonphysical camp (only inferable, not directly measurable) yet, we accept them because they help us remain logically consistent and represent the current best fit within (are sometimes required by) our model of physical reality.

We can build useful and valuable material, conceptual, theoretical, and spiritual results based on the knowledge and understanding of inferred nonphysical objects. Successful operational experimentation with nonphysical phenomena that are not acceptable to traditional science (such as energy and information transfers within NPMR or PMR that appear to the PMR observer to be acausal) often employs the methodologies that physicists use to work with inferred objects such as neutrinos, as well as the processes that scientists use to develop more purely conceptual objects like wave packets or strings. Science is science; many of the same logical approaches to discovery work as well in NPMR as they do in PMR. The major difference is that NPMR objects are not accepted by traditional scientists because they do not fit the little picture PMR reality model. For the most part, this is because the type of data gathered from NPMR and the process for obtaining and validating it, is by their nature and design, mostly incompatible with PMR's traditional narrowly focused scientific methodology which is based upon a mystical belief in the universality of PMR causality. (See Chapters 13 and 14 of Book 2, and Chapter 2 of this book for supporting detail.)

Conflicting with the nineteenth and twentieth century's most precious intellectual jewel, the scientific method, is not necessarily the kiss of death to an open mind. The scientific method is a terrific tool within the realm to which it applies.

Our most successful scientific models and processes have turned out to have a limited validity, including classical mechanics (large slow objects), special relativity (fast objects, but no gravity), the flat earth (short distances), or a stable physical universe (short times). Likewise, the scientific method has a limited validity. Our refusal to appreciate those limitations has trapped our awareness in PMR. The time is ripe, once again, to raise our thinking up to the next level of generality, thus greatly expanding our vision of what is possible.

An expanded view of a scientific method that contains the traditional scientific method as a subset would also better encompass and support some presently accepted fields including medicine, psychology, sociology, and ethics, as well as the nontraditional, but equally serious, fields of cosmology, epistemology, and ontology. For example, when was the last time the Centers for Disease Control and Prevention (CDC) performed an objective scientific public health **experiment** with a highly contagious deadly infectious disease? Obviously, the CDC cannot apply a traditional scientific methodology to the study of fatal infectious diseases. Instead it must rely on indirect statistical inference – the same methodology that is often used to produce an objective evaluation of subjective experience.

A generalized scientific method must be rigorous and testable, as well as produce consistent and meaningful results; the requirement for testable rigor and meaningfulness in no way eliminates the value and usefulness of subjective input.

Formally defining a practical generalized scientific method is not within the scope or intent of this trilogy, but an informal description of what needs to be included is discussed in the previous chapter and in Chapter 13, Book 2.

Your attitude is important. Avoid getting twisted around the preciseness, accuracy or the appropriateness of how the definitions within this chapter apply to your particular view of, and beliefs about, the world. Keep in mind that we are trying to effect a communication of big ideas within this trilogy, not specify the number of hairs in a gnat's eyebrow. If you get the big ideas, some fuzziness is acceptable; precision and clarity comes with personal experience in the larger reality. Trying to solidly grasp what lies beyond your experiential reach is what pulls you up by your bootstraps, but overreaching coupled with high expectations will always lead to more frustration than progress.

If you have a fuzzy idea of what I mean here by PMR and NPMR, and can catch the spirit of the observations in the next chapter, you will be able to find a meaningful view of the Big Picture.

Again, do **not** feel **required** to believe or disbelieve or to pass final judgment on what you read. It is permissible, even preferable, to let the concepts contained herein be seeds, possibilities that hang out in the fertile ground of some obscure corner of your mind. Who knows, one day spontaneous germination may be triggered by a future experience, a deepened understanding, or through meditation, cogitation, or personal study. (Satori often occurs in violent brainstorms that contain lots of blunder-thunder and frightening-lightning – but only if the seed is there). On the other hand, **you are absolutely required** to be scientifically (not driven by belief or fear) critical and skeptical of what you find here, or **your** Big TOE will not grow. Without a careful application of open minded skepticism you will miss much of the opportunity presented by *My Big TOE*.

4

■ ■ ■

Some Observations

■ ■ ■

These thirteen observations reflect my experience exploring NPMR and provide a short summary of the data necessary to support the conceptual development of the Mechanics of Reality. They are written here as unsupported blunt summary statements. Sections 2, 3, and 4 of *My Big TOE* thoroughly develop the logical foundation upon which these thirteen observations rest.

If your personal experience does not clearly encompass and support these statements, consider them to be stated assumptions that may or may not be critical to what follows in the next nine chapters. Keep in mind that belief or disbelief in the correctness of these observations is at best irrelevant, while a skeptical open-mind is absolutely necessary. If, on the other hand, your personal experience validates these notions, they will appear to be simple facts that stand on their own requiring neither belief nor conjecture for support. Regardless of the level of experience you bring to this discussion, my advice is to trudge on through this chapter without being too fussy. The supporting details are contained in the first two books of this trilogy and will not be repeated here; this is simply a terse summary and review of what has been established elsewhere within *MY Big TOE*.

1. PMR is not the only, and not necessarily the primary, nor the most important reality. Each reality exists within its own calculation-space or dimension. All realities are not necessarily independent. There can be connections and dependencies between realities along with rules governing their interactions.

2. As shown in Figure 5-1, there are multiple, loosely related, weakly interacting reality systems within NPMR (each $NPMR_n$ where n = 1, 2, 3... represents a specific reality system). Each of the $NPMR_n$ seems to be

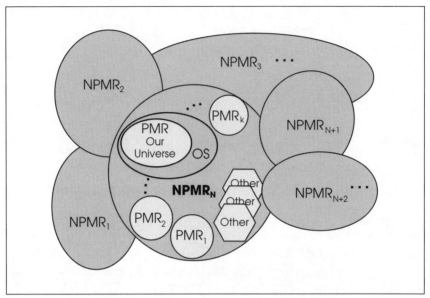

Figure 5.1: Reality Systems: The Big Picture

organized as separate ongoing experiments in consciousness. Each experiment has its own objectives, protocols, conditions, timeline, and purpose.

3. One of these reality systems within NPMR, say $NPMR_N$ (where the index **n** takes the specific value N), contains our PMR as a subset. $NPMR_N$ is a spiritual (quality of consciousness) system experimenting with the evolutionary **potential** of consciousness. $NPMR_N$ contains many other reality subsets besides PMR. Some of these other subsets constitute physical universes similar (space-time-matter based) to our PMR (we are nonphysical to the beings of these realities) while others are very different from our PMR (not based on space-time-matter). Within each of these reality subsets, there are types and classes of beings living within the rules of their own physics, psychology, and sociology. Our System (OS) of reality contains PMR and a portion of $NPMR_N$. Figure 5-1 shows only one small portion of the larger consciousness ecosystem.

4. In $NPMR_N$, the goal for each sentient being is to learn, grow, and evolve through interaction (making choices) with others: The intent driving our choices can range from good to evil. We make free will choices in the process of interacting with other sentient beings, and the quality of these choices alters the entropy of our consciousness through a self-modifying feedback system. Personal growth is required to effect our entropy reducing contribution to the larger consciousness cycle.

To optimize entropy loss, one must understand how consciousness evolves under varying conditions. Does all consciousness eventually end up love-like (the optimal result) or exactly the opposite; or does a consciousness system eventually become chaotic or perhaps find some stable equilibrium state in between these extremes? Is it possible to isolate and stabilize the optimal conditions for growing or evolving high quality consciousness, thus optimizing the efficiency of the consciousness cycle?

5. All consciousness in $NPMR_N$ is "netted." It is as though each entity in $NPMR_N$ has a unique URL (Uniform Resource Locator or web address) in a gigantic, but finite, Reality Wide Web (RWW). Thus, as a subset, all beings in our particular PMR are also netted together – on a Local Area Network (LAN) so to speak – as well as connected (connections between LANs) with the rest of OS and all other $NPMR_N$ residents. Connections to the $NPMR_n$ and beyond are likewise available, but not particularly important to this discussion.

6. An individual in PMR can be aware of NPMR through his or her mind – the nonphysical part of one's being. The mind is the doorway through which you must pass to experience NPMR. NPMR is, if anything, more real than PMR (semantics in the service of an impish smile) because it contains a more fundamental (less constrained) reality of which PMR is only one of many subsets.

7. An individual in PMR, once fully aware in $NPMR_N$, can access and filter the RWW net described above with his or her intent. An individual can access any web-page-entity on this RWW net by using his or her intent (which requires unique knowledge and identification of the URL being sought). One navigates with one's intent. A person's intent is also his or her filter; without this filter one would have difficulty dealing with all the information at once.

Explorers must learn their way around by exploring the RWW – for the same general reasons that force you to personally explore the WWW (reading about it and being an interactive part of it are two entirely different experiences). Experience, carefully filtered by a scientific method (repeatable evidential data collection) that sorts external signal from internal noise, leads to the knowledge that forms the basis for a larger set of productive and meaningful possible intents. Those who wish to access information, objects, or entities on the RWW consciousness network need to educate themselves within and about $NPMR_N$. Carefully validated firsthand experience must be acquired through a step by step exploratory process.

8. Individual communications between sentient entities are telepathic. Additionally, within a given PMR, communication using sensory data (such as sight, sound, touch, smell, and taste) typically functions in parallel with telepathy to some degree.

9. People in PMR who are unaware (or mostly unaware) within NPMR, can use and experience this net if they are connected strongly enough (large enough signal-to-noise) and with enough clear intent (interest) to produce a crosstalk or bleedthrough into their consciousness (typically perceived as intuition or precognitive dreams). Signals come from NPMR with varying amplitudes while an individual produces most of his own interfering noise.

10. Telepathic communications and other communications through the $NPMR_N$ net are not affected by the **apparent** distance or volume between the sender and the receiver, nor limited by light speed. Communication content flows across dimensional barriers without difficulty.

11. Beings in all PMRs within $NPMR_N$ have portions or extensions of themselves that also (simultaneously) exist in $NPMR_N$. The body in PMR is essentially sustained through its connection to $NPMR_N$. By manipulating energy (the ability to reorganize bits) in $NPMR_N$, one can affect the body in PMR. Thus follow many effects from mental or psychic healing to voodoo. The energy body in $NPMR_N$ can be viewed from various "frequencies" (like looking at something with X-ray, infrared, or ultraviolet light) to reveal different aspects of itself. (I apologize to all the scientists and engineers for using the frequency metaphor, but it is the best analogy I can come up with.) The energy body is easily manipulated by intention.

12. Intent seems to have the qualities of magnitude (intensity), frequency (is tunable), and clarity (signal to noise ratio).

13. The energy body in $NPMR_N$ does not die when the physical body dies; it can manifest another body in PMR (or some other suitable reality) if it needs or wants one.

5

■ ■ ■

A Model of Reality and Time
Incrementing Time in Simulations

■ ■ ■

To understand reality one must understand time. During the next six chapters, we will use the notations "delta-t" and "DELTA-t" extensively. Because this notation is borrowed from the field of mathematics, it may seem strange to some, but do not be put off by that. This chapter provides an explanation of incrementing time in simulations to the mathematically challenged and introduces a unique perspective on the nature of time to the Big Picture reality challenged. The words "delta" and "DELTA" represent the upper and lower case Greek letter of the same name. They are spelled out to avoid using abstract symbols that might inadvertently trigger mathephobia or other related mental techno-blocks. This is easy – you'll see.

Traditional mathematical notation places the Greek letter delta next to a variable (some quantity that changes) to represent an increment (small change) in that variable. I use it here because many people are familiar with this notation. If you are not, don't worry, the concept is simple and explained in detail below. "DELTA-t" and "delta-t" are simply names for two different increments (small chunks) of time.

In an iterative dynamic simulation, such as the calculation of the position of a fired artillery round (or a thrown ball) as a function of time, one starts with the equations of motion (equations giving position as a function of time) and the initial conditions at time t=0. The first time through the computational process loop, one lets t = (delta-t) and then calculates position – next time through t = 2•(delta-t), next time through t = 3•(delta-t), next time through t = 4•(delta-t), and so on. You calculate a new position of the object (artillery round or ball) for each time t, which is one delta-t larger than the previous value of t. Consequently, time, in your calculation of position, progresses forward by increments (small discontinuous jumps) of delta-t.

Your simulation can approximate continuous time, and thus continuous motion, by making the size of delta-t very small. The cumulative sum over the delta-t is called "simulation time" because it drives the dynamic simulation, (as opposed to "real-time" which is what is measured by the clock on the computer room wall).

If the equations were complex enough and delta-t were small enough and the computer slow enough, it could take several hours of real-time to progress the artillery rounds trajectory through only a few seconds of simulation time (perhaps only a few hundred feet of a much longer trajectory) within the computer simulation. On the other hand, relatively simple equations in a very fast computer using a larger delta-t might simulate a one minute long trajectory (such as the trajectory of a large artillery round) in only a few tenths of a second of real-time.

The simulation can be paused any amount of real-time between consecutive time increments and subsequently started up again without disturbing the results of the simulation. These concepts involving notions of dynamic simulation and time will be important later on. It is good to understand them now while the context is simple.

Consider a large simulation that contains smaller simulations within it. For example, let's imagine a simulated war containing several simultaneous interactive battles. Such a system simulation may contain a subset of code (subroutine) that simulates a specific battle, which has within it another iterative subset of code (lower level subroutine) that simulates a specific armor battalion's activity within that battle, which has within it a yet another iterative subset of code (even lower level subroutine) that simulates an artillery shell fired by that armor battalion. We now have four nested (one inside the other) levels of interdependent subroutines (1-overall war, 2-specific battles, 3-specific battalions, 4-individual artillery trajectories) iterating their way sequentially to produce the simulated war.

The collection of algorithms that describe the interdependencies between levels (specify the assumptions, initial conditions, tactics, rules of engagement, and describe the performance of each subsystem and component) are said to model or simulate the war. A properly integrated collection of such models, along with the structure of the code that orders and propagates interactive logical events, passes data, collects results, and increments time, defines the overall war game or simulation. This is how computers are used to simulate a set of interactive activities or a dynamic process.

All the interdependent loops are iterated sequentially. Loops that have no interdependency may be incremented in parallel (simultaneously). Each level and each process within each level progresses its own dynamic activity by one delta-t at a time. As activities are completed (decisions made, trajectories flown, damage assessed, troops and equipment moved, and ammunition depleted) information is passed back and forth among the four levels. The results and implications of this information are used to make choices, continue or modify processes, and keep score. Thus, as the simulation time progresses delta-t by delta-t, the simulated war grinds on.

The practical size of delta-t depends on the required accuracy and the speed of the fastest elements in our model. A typical delta-t might be 0.00001 seconds if the precise locations (to within a centimeter) of things such as artillery rounds and missiles were important. In this simulation, delta-t defines the **fundamental quantum of simulation-time.** If the fastest thing in our war simulation (an ancient war perhaps, or a modern one where all the gadgets don't work) was a man running through the bushes with a spear, a delta-t of 0.1 second would probably be small enough.

Would simulating an ancient (spear throwing) or slow moving war (requiring a time base of no more than delta-t = 0.1 second) with our modern war simulator (that ticks off time in 0.00001 second increments) be a problem? No: There is no problem as long as we are simulating something that can be adequately modeled with time increments that are **equal to or larger** than 0.00001 seconds. It would make no sense to simulate the position of a running man every 0.00001 seconds. It might allow for a more detailed and complex model of the man (including blinks, burps, hair motion, progressive cell damage, and twitches), however, a man's movement within that small of a time increment (0.00001 sec) is completely inconsequential to the war.

What we would most likely do is use our previous coarse or low fidelity man-movement-model and increment it by a single 0.1 second increment every 10000 (10^4) ticks of our simulation time clock. Our war game's fundamental quantum of simulation-time is still equal to 0.00001 seconds or 10^{-5} sec. We are now incrementing our man-model in 0.1 second increments as a subroutine within a larger model (outer loop) that iterates every 0.00001 seconds. This will turn out to be a crucial concept later.

This more efficiently incremented, low-fidelity man-model (it remains detailed enough to define troop movement as a function of terrain) is purposely designed to be only as accurate, and incremented only as often, as it needs to be to serve the purpose that is intended by the overall simulation. Likewise, the loops and subroutines that represent various players in the simulation are provided the dynamic granularity (increment size) that their function requires. The one with the smallest required increment serves as the metronome (the fundamental quantum of time within our simulation) for all the others.

Let's put this all together into one big war simulation. We will have man-model subroutines that are incremented by one tenth of a second every 10^4 increments of our fundamental simulation time. We will also have tank-model subroutines that are incremented by a hundredth of a second every 10^3 ticks of the fundamental clock. We might have aircraft-model subroutines that are incremented by a thousandth of a second every 10^2 ticks of the fundamental clock and missile subroutines that are incremented every third tick of the fundamental clock, and perhaps a nuclear damage propagation subroutine that will be incremented (evaluated) every tick of the fundamental clock.

In this simulation, the master loop or simulation driver is the one requiring the smallest time increment. The guy in charge (outermost loop) is the one with the smallest time increment. The local time inside the man-model-loop jumps ahead one tenth-second at a time. The low fidelity simulated men who live in that local reality measure a **quantum of their time** as one-tenth second. **From their perspective**, real-time accumulates in increments of one-tenth second. One-tenth second is their local time quanta. If they could become sentient and learn to program, they could decide to simulate the growth of their hair and toenails because these functions change slowly compared to their time quantum.

Let's summarize the most useful ideas that have been generated by this discussion of dynamic simulations. Some of the time loops, subroutines, or dimensions of our big picture (entire war) simulation are iterated at faster rates than others. **Apparent** real-time is relative to each loop's perspective or local reality.

Within a given **local** reality, we can **only** perceive events which produce effects that are significant over one **local** time quanta or more, thus rendering the activities of faster loops (smaller time quanta) invisible and incomprehensible. Within the hierarchy of causality (simulations within simulations or dimensions within dimensions), the master or outermost loop that drives everything else is defined as the one with the highest fundamental frequency (highest sampling rate or rate of iteration), which is the same as saying it has the smallest quantum of time.

Bells should be going off in your head relating this discussion of computer simulation to the discussion of AUM's fundamental frequency and time quantum, and the differing sized quanta of time in NPMR and PMR

(Chapter 31, Book 1). Each higher level of simulation, with its smaller time quanta, represents a larger perspective, a base of authority and control, and collects, processes and synthesizes the activities and results created by its lower level (inner) subordinate simulations. Dynamic timing loops within loops within loops, all interconnected and building one upon the other at various levels of scale. Do you notice the fractal-like characteristics of time loops within your dynamic reality? Do you get a glimmer of how everything is interrelated and interconnected within a generalized dynamic consciousness-evolution fractal ecosystem?

You will see later that what I define as delta-t represents the outer (controlling) loop of **our immediate** reality within OS. delta-t is used to calculate probable realities and is referred to as simulation time; it is related to time in NPMR. On the other hand, DELTA-t, a larger time increment, is defined as the increment that accumulates our PMR time, our apparent real-time. From a larger perspective, DELTA-t drives a lower level simulation (with its larger time increment) incremented only once every so many ticks of the overall simulation time clock within The Big Computer. Did I infer that you, me, and our entire universe, are simulated beings and objects? Yes: you will see that it is illuminating, consistent, and useful to model our reality that way. Throughout *My Big TOE*, I have dangled this idea of a simulated reality in front of you; as strange as it may seem, it will make more sense later on.

Recall that in Chapter 31, Book 1, I explained that time is quantized, meaning that time progresses by discrete increments rather than continuously, and that our time is an artificial construct created by AUM to define the space-time part of itself. In this section, you will see how quantized time loops allow us to create our reality, maintain a living history, and make choices that enable us to learn and to grow the quality of our consciousness (evolve our spiritual quality toward satisfying the goals of our existence). A digital reality offers up many interesting attributes.

You will soon see that time is not a fundamental property of the thread that is woven to produce the fabric of reality, but instead is merely a measurement construct, a tool for implementing organization and defining patterns, more related to the action of the machine that does the weaving than to the thread itself. Each cycle of the loom represents another time increment as thread after thread is added to produce the seemingly continuous fabric of our PMR 3D space-time experience.

The action of the machine, the process of weaving, should not be confused with the three-dimensional experience of the space-time fabric it creates. Nor should the fabric be seen to weave itself through some spontaneous mystical or magical process wherein time is created in the present moment **without** the need of factory or loom or the energy that makes them run, much less the design and purpose of the process. That space-time is spontaneously self-created from nothing – a self-woven, 4D fabric containing all past, present, and future events – is basically what most scientists believe these days because they cannot perceive the higher dimensions where the loom, mill, and the energy that runs them resides. In fact, our present science is based on the fundamental implicit assumption that the loom and mill cannot possibly exist, or be relevant, because they lie beyond our direct objective 3D perception of a 4D space-time.

Thus, today's scientists have painted themselves into a corner dependent upon reality mysteriously creating itself – a **mystical** belief-based concept they are greatly dissatisfied with and do not like to talk about – a fundamental failure of scientific understanding long swept under the rug of objective respectability.

On the other hand, the theists are content, as they have been for 10,000 years, to offer up their one pat answer for all situations and occasions: God does it. Meanwhile, the fabric of space-time continues to apparently weave itself out of nothing as we stumble in circles in pursuit of a Big Picture that we can somehow miraculously extract from our little picture. And that is where we are today, ladies and gentlemen, and where we have been for the last forty years since general relativity and quantum mechanics dropped the first shoe (told us in no uncertain terms that our physical reality was delusional). Einstein tried to lead us out of that wilderness with Unified Field Theory but could not find his way through the impenetrable cultural belief fog that obscured every avenue of escape. Belief blindness is as absolute as any blindness.

That a higher dimensional structure may not leave **physical** footprints is not that difficult to understand. Einstein was correctly looking for nonphysical footprints in his Unified Field Theory where mass was nothing more than higher intensity field strength. His error was looking for continuous fields within the space-time construct. He did not grasp the digital nature of reality – that space and time are quantized – and that space-time itself was only a local phenomenon, a virtual little picture reality dependent upon a more fundamental digital energy field called consciousness. He did not understand the primacy of consciousness as the fundamental substance, energy, or organization underlying existence. Instead of seeing space-time as primordial physics, a set of relationships and definitions, a rule-set, a construct of consciousness, he thought that space-time itself was the fundamental field. Consciousness is fundamental. Space-time is derived from a conscious intent to constrain individuated subsets of consciousness to a specific experience-base which we call PMR.

Even if Einstein had figured that out in the 1950s, his peers would have written him off as having lost it. He would have most likely ended his career in ridicule. Today we are much more familiar with the potential of the digital sciences. Perhaps now, in the twenty-first century, scientists will have the requisite vision to see and understand the paradigm shifts that are required to support a unified theory of reality. Perhaps non-scientists will recognize the Big Picture first and eventually bring the scientists along.

Tracking the nonphysical footprints of a more fundamental reality through the consciousness wilderness is what *My Big TOE* is all about – and you do not need to be a physicist or mathematician to get it because the details and explanations are not little picture logic puzzles that exist only within PMR. In the Big Picture, a deep understanding of reality is not the exclusive preserve of the scientist and mathematician: That state of affairs, where scientists are the high priests of reality, is a little picture phenomenon only. When it comes to understanding the Big Picture, there are no academic prerequisites. You do not need to wait for the science guys and mathematicians to lead this parade – march on to the beat of your own experience and inner knowing and they will eventually follow your lead.

It is as though the objects in the simulation (local AI Guy's within each subroutine) have become sentient but can't perceive outside their time loop level and consequently, are oblivious to (or vehemently deny) the bigger picture. They live in their limited universe paying homage to the Loop Gods who occasionally provide fresh input data and to whom they offer up the results of their efforts.

6
■ ■ ■

A Model of Reality and Time
The Big Computer (TBC)

■ ■ ■

We have previously discussed the likely origins of an immense digital computational capacity based upon binary reality cells that are the fundamental constituent of aware consciousness or mind. In Section 2 (Chapters 26, 27, and 28 of Book 1) you learned how and why AUO would naturally evolve binary (distorted vs. non-distorted) reality cells in support of organizing and exploring (in the evolutionary sense) increasing complexity and developing awareness. You also learned how AUM would further refine its computational and memory part to develop intention, move from dim awareness to bright awareness, and to implement and track its *gedanken* experiments in consciousness.

Awareness cannot grow, progress, learn, or evolve past a very rudimentary level without the organizing influence of time. The words "learn" and "grow" imply the passage, or incrementing of time – there must exist a before state and an after state if awareness, or any system for that matter, has the potential to learn or grow. The notion of the possibility of change is dependent upon the existence of at least a rudimentary time. As you will soon see, our discrete (quantized) time-based reality has evolved (has been designed) to provide us with an opportunity to learn, and to provide AUM with optimized results from its *gedanken* experiments concerning the optimization of evolutionary process.

The complex configuration of digital energy (organization) and self-organizing process we call consciousness forms the foundation of reality in the form of an interactive consciousness-evolution fractal ecosystem simulation where what is actual and what is simulated are one in the same.

You can conceptualize TBC as a tiny piece of the computational and memory part of AUM that is used, among other things, to actualize and maintain the reality of OS and its offspring. For the purpose of explaining consciousness, quantized time (past, present, and future), time travel, free will, rule-sets, space-time, precognition, telepathic communication, remote viewing, ego, love and much more in this model of reality, I evoke only those attributes of this celestial computer that our PMR computers have. In other words, this super computer in $NPMR_N$ that I have assumed into existence primarily differs from the functional computer on our desktops by size (memory), computational speed, reliability, and reasonably good software – that's all.

▶ This aside is for all the computer geeks in the reading audience who are waving their hands in the air and have troubled expressions on their faces. Others can skip to the end or take a short break until the computer wizards catch up.

It may make more sense to the computer literate if they imagine that TBC is composed of fully netted, massively parallel arrays of clustered processors with integrated, shared, and stand alone super fast memory running within a highly efficient self-evolving AUM-operating-system that is beyond all imagination. In other words, if you can imagine that the AUM-digital-consciousness-thing is completely beyond your imagination, you have taken the first step toward understanding the depth of what you don't know.

In an operational sense, one might say that AUM **is** the operating system as well as the computer and the application software. This AUM-thing is an almost infinite (from our perspective) living, evolving, conscious, sentient computer and operating system that develops its own software. At a minimum, it inhabits as well as defines and creates all the digital mind-space (reality) that we have the potential to even vaguely comprehend; other than that, it is an inconsequential piss-ant.

When I say that TBC is like the computer on your desktop, I am referring to the fundamental functional building blocks of binary cells, memory, instruction-sets, processors, data flow mechanics, and operating system control, not the specific design of these things or the system architecture. Think of a computer in the most generic terms possible and take care not to limit your imagination by what you presently know about computers. ◀

TBC should not be thought of as the big mainframe in the sky, or as the OS Department server within N Division, but as a metaphor describing the fundamental nature of the process and functionality (computation, memory, and rules) required to implement our reality.

TBC is a real thing; we relate to it more by its process and functionality (discussed in this section) than by its construction and design (discussed in Sections 2 and 4) – the same way most of us interact with our desktop computers. We don't relate to chips and basic chip-level instruction-sets, but instead see our computers in terms of their functionality and the processes they implement. We are primarily interested in the processes we need to follow to optimize our interaction with them.

The most surprising thing is that TBC, the implementer of all reality within $NPMR_N$, represents nothing mystical, no magic, just a huge (but finite), fast, mundane number cruncher running excellent, but not necessarily perfect, software. The mundaneness of TBC is, by itself, remarkable and interesting. Digital processing is digital processing however cleverly or efficiently it is implemented.

The software and operating system might reasonably be construed to represent the intent of AUM, or one may understand it as the result of evolutionary pressure working upon a growing, experimenting, evolving AUM-consciousness-system-being-thing exploring all its possible states. TBC, dedicated to $NPMR_N$, represents only one small part of AUM's computational part – other reality systems have their own computational and memory resources. All are interconnected because they are of one consciousness. We use the terms AUM, EBC, and TBC to express differing levels of digital functionality, however, at the root, they are not separate parts. Imagine a single evolving digital system serving multiple functions simultaneously.

Trying to differentiate between the larger consciousness system and yourself can be misleading – the boundaries are only functional. AUM, TBC, PMR, and you are all manifestations of a single consciousness. Each differs by function and purpose and is circumscribed by its specific constraints, yet all are of one continuous consciousness – like the lumps in a sheet.

Though the greater consciousness ecosystem is vast and ranges far beyond our view, there is much that lies within the reach of our direct experience and understanding. Humans have barely taken the first baby step toward knowing what is within our ability to know. As we continue to play our part in the larger consciousness cycle of entropy reduction, it is our right as well as our duty, to explore everything between where we are today and the far edge of our potential – to become aware and active participants in the Big Picture and full partners in the evolution of ourselves and AUM.

7

■ ■ ■

A Model of Reality and Time
Probable Reality Surfaces
The Simulated Probable Future
Real-time, Our System,
State Vectors, and History

■ ■ ■

1. Probable Reality

Let us begin this discussion of time and the mechanics of OS (our collective Big Picture **local** reality) in the PMR present and slowly work toward a more generalized concept of past and future. Join me here in the present moment and let us see what is happening in $NPMR_N$ to support our sense of reality-present. The Big Computer (TBC) has captured in its database the state of being of OS at this moment. This includes all the objects and energy in the universe as well as all the significant choices that all the relevant sentient beings within OS have at this moment. Later in this chapter we will more specifically, and in more detail, define the set of information that specifies this state of being or "state vector" of Our System (OS).

TBC can now compute everything that could possibly happen next (we will explore this thought more thoroughly later). Additionally, it has accumulated a history file of past behaviors relative to similar choices and can thus compute the likelihood of occurrence (probabilities) of each of the possible things that could happen next. Many of the current choices are dependent on a likely interaction with the choices that all relevant and significant others (including themselves) made the moment (or many moments) before. All possible interactions are defined and evaluated with respect to all possible choices and arrangements of objects and energy, as well as against a complete set of history based likelihoods (expectation values).

During the time between successive increments of PMRs quantum of time (DELTA-t), TBC has computed OS's probable future – what OS will probably be like during the next **M** (**m** = 1, 2, 3, ...**M,** where **M** is an integer) iterations of DELTA-t. Thus within TBC, the dynamic OS has been simulated and its future state, the one that will most likely appear during the next DELTA-t (**m** = 1), has been predicted based on the results of the present state of OS after the last DELTA-t. This OS simulation is run again (**m** = 2) with the results from the previous predictive simulation (**m** = 1) used as input, and the probable outcomes and expectation values for the following DELTA-t are predicted as output.

Each successive output (predicting the state of OS out into the future one more DELTA-t) becomes the input for the next predictive calculation. This process is continued **M** times until TBC has progressed the model of OS out as far in time as it finds useful. The probable OS state vector generated after each iteration (for each value of **m**) during the dynamic simulation of what is most likely to happen in OS during the next DELTA-t is saved in TBC. Remember that we are doing all **M** iterations between actual increments of DELTA-t.

As displayed in Text Box 5-1 below, the iterative process would operate in the following manner. First, a new DELTA-t increment is initiated resulting in the initiation of a new OS state vector. Then, all free will choices and material and energetic changes that define the activity that creates this new OS are made. The choices and changes, once made, define a new and unique state vector (or more simply, "state") of OS that is associated with

---

1. DELTA-t is incremented.
2. Free-will choices, material changes, and energy changes are made, defining a new OS state vector associated with the current DELTA-t.
3. The new OS state vector is compared to the previous one and to the predicted one.
4. All actualized changes between the new and previous OS states are recorded. Predictive algorithms and data bases are updated and improved.
5. TBC calculates M sequential probable future states of the new OS by running a delta-t sub-loop.

Text Box 5.1: The OS/DELTA-t Loop

this particular DELTA-t. TBC now compares the new OS state vector to the previous one and records the actualized changes. It also compares the newly actualized state to the predicted state and makes the necessary adjustments required to improve the accuracy of future predictions.

Next, TBC calculates **M** potential future states (of the new OS state). These **M** calculations (made sequentially one value of **m** at a time) project (simulate) what is most likely to happen during the next **M** increments of DELTA-t. The first (**m** = 1) potential future state (probable reality) of OS is computed in TBC based on the latest actualized (actually happened) input data generated by the choices made during the current state of OS.

This predictive simulation of the state of OS, which progresses by iterating **m** from 1 to **M**, creates a set of sequential probable realities describing the probable future of OS. The subroutine or iterative loop we are using to generate future probable realities of OS must, because it is a dynamic simulation tracking changes, operate on its own time base, and that time base must utilize a much smaller time increment than DELTA-t. This smaller time increment, which we will call delta-t, is associated with a quantum of time in $NPMR_N$. Utilizing a time increment (delta-t) that is very much smaller than the PMR quantum of time (DELTA-t), allows us to model the dynamics of OS (which is a subset of $NPMR_N$) in enough detail so that we can predict the most likely state of OS for each value of **m**. Thus, delta-t is the fundamental quantum of OS simulation time.

The OS state vector simulation runs through its internal calculations using the smaller $NPMR_N$ time quanta (delta-t) until it eventually converges to a predicted future state of OS for every value of **m**. It should be clear that the time increment DELTA-t is composed of or contains some large integer number of $NPMR_N$ time quanta delta-t, and that the computation of the probable future of OS through **M** successive generations occurs between successive increments (DELTA-t) of our PMR real-time.

Now that a set of **M** successive generations of probable future realities has been determined, TBC next records the entire OS state vector representing all significant possibilities and probabilities existing within OS. This step is discussed in further detail in Topic 9 of this chapter. The final step of the OS DELTA-t loop iterates the process by returning the loop back to the first step. DELTA-t is incremented again, and the entire process is repeated for the new DELTA-t.

Let's back our perspective out one more level for a peek at an even bigger picture. Though it lies somewhat beyond our immediate perception, contemplate the concept that delta-t is incremented only after so many ticks of a smaller, more fundamental time increment. We know that delta-t is a small time-increment ($NPMR_N$ time base) used to simulate what is most likely to happen in OS during future DELTA-t time increments. It is used to simulate probable future states of OS and to increment a larger DELTA-t (the OS DELTA-t loop). Furthermore, consider that delta-t is incremented only after so many ticks of a smaller time increment that is used to simulate probable future states of $NPMR_N$ (the $NPMR_N$ delta-t loop).

Because NPMR is an outer loop to $NPMR_N$ (where OS lives), it makes sense that NPMR runs on a smaller time quantum than $NPMR_N$. Thus, just as the OS DELTA-t loop must have the smaller delta-t as its fundamental quantum of simulation time, the $NPMR_N$ delta-t loop must likewise have a smaller time increment than delta-t as its fundamental quantum of simulation time. Keep in mind that NPMR is a superset of $NPMR_N$; also that $NPMR_N$ is a superset of OS and that OS is a superset of our PMR (OS is comprised of our PMR plus a portion of $NPMR_N$).

The fundamental increment of a bigger-picture simulation-time represents an outside loop that provides a larger perspective than $NPMR_N$. The increment of time of such an outside or higher-level loop must be smaller than the fundamental unit of time in $NPMR_N$. Expanding this idea, it is clear that the fundamental increment of NPMR **simulation-time** may likewise be smaller than the fundamental unit of time in NPMR itself.

Is all this clear or is your head spinning a little? If you are a tad confused, it might be helpful to go back to Chapter 5 of this book and refresh your memory on the subject of incrementing time within simulations. Additionally, a glance at Figure 5-1 (at the beginning of Chapter 4 in this book) and a peek ahead at the discussion of the Even Bigger Computer (EBC) at the end of Chapter 11 might help clarify this bigger picture. Otherwise, if you feel that you mostly get it, absolutely do get it, or don't want to get it any better than you've gotten it, simply go on. In this situation, continuing on (though you find yourself in a light fog) is much better than becoming terminally frustrated. Hang in there, the text gets less technical later.

The predictions produced by calculating the probable state of Our System $\mathbf{m} \cdot (DELTA\text{-}t)$ into the probable future become less accurate the further out in time they go. However, because our computer (TBC) and its software are so good, it can progress PMR time out for many years (**M** can be arbitrarily large) in less than a nano-nanosecond.

The result is a PMR space-time event surface in TBC calculation-space. TBC is only a subset of a greater digital mind-space. For we 3D creatures constrained to visualize our mental concepts within an experiential 3D structure, it is easier to think about a planar (two dimensional) event surface extending out in the dimension of simulated time with probability values (of particular events) on the vertical (up) axis – perhaps something similar to the surface shown in Figure 5-2. The horizontal plane, upon which the peaks rest, contain values of time, from t = 0 at the origin to some simulated future time **m**•(DELTA-t), the far edge of the event surface being at the time corresponding to **M**•(DELTA-t).

Events near the present moment typically have the highest probability values (sharp tall peaks). The further out we go in time the flatter the surface gets; peaks tend to broaden and lose height exhibiting very small, rather diffuse, probability values or likelihoods. Nevertheless, there may exist a few well formed and sizable (> .8 expectation value) peaks rather far out in time. You might want to take another peek at Figure 5-2.

In summary, TBC generates a complete set of probable realities covering everything (choices, things, and energy) most likely to happen between each DELTA-t and the next one. TBC then saves and stores these results describing every unique probable state of OS corresponding to each simulated DELTA-t for each value of **m**. This complete set of probable realities going out **M**•(DELTA-t) in our PMR real-time are regenerated after each actual increment of DELTA-t.

I have used the term reality state vector ("reality state," or simply "state" for short) to mean the total description or specification of the

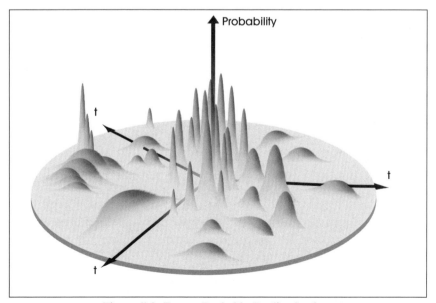

Figure 5.2: Future Probable Reality Surface

state of existing choices, things, and energy that defines OS at the end of a DELTA-t. Later I will define more precisely what a reality state vector is (Topic 9 below) and describe the process that generates them (Chapters 8 through 10 of this book), but first there are a few more basic concepts to be introduced.

2. Introducing Real-Time – What Our Clocks Measure in PMR

What appears to be real-time is dependant on the relative reality level or loop location of your local perspective within the Big Picture. PMR real-time appears to be continuous but actually progresses incrementally by iterating the small time increment DELTA-t. During DELTA-t, beings, objects, and energy move and change, free will is exercised, and significant choices are made in PMR. Most changes were as predicted by the $m = 1$ calculation of expectation values, but some were not. Adjustments are made. Again, TBC runs the delta-t based OS simulation. Again it re-computes all the probable realities – OS state vector expectation values through M generations – creating, updating, and storing the event surface as subsequent calculations progress.

TBC's computing requirements are not as horrendous as one might first think: Clever software finds updating the complete set ($m = 1$ to $m = M$) of probable realities to be much easier (merely dealing with changes and errors and their downstream impacts) than re-computing everything from scratch every time. It should be clear that what we sense and measure as time (our real-time) moves forward in PMR by successive increments of DELTA-t, while probable realities (future expectations) are computed within TBC to **project** the probable future states of OS through M successive simulated increments of DELTA-t.

Recall from Section 2 (Chapter 31, Book 1) that the quantum of time in $NPMR_N$ is much smaller than the quantum of time (DELTA-t) in OS and PMR. Thus, during a single DELTA-t of PMR real-time, $NPMR_N$ has many time increments (quanta) ticking away in which calculations can be made, probabilities computed, and probable reality surfaces generated. Also, recall that in Chapter 5 of this book we described how the flow of time in a subset or subroutine of the simulation was dependent on its outer controlling loop and that the simulation could be paused, stopped, and then restarted (relative to the clock in the computer room) without causing any effects within the simulation.

AUM's fundamental clock is the clock on the computer room wall and we are a subset of $NPMR_N$ within a subset of NPMR. In other words, $NPMR_N$ controls PMR's outer controlling loop, while NPMR controls

$NPMR_N$'s outer loop. The process just described (the generation of OS, resulting from incrementing our real-time quantum DELTA-t and the calculation of our probable futures) raised to the next level of generality, allows for freewill choices among sentient residents of $NPMR_N$. In a similar process to that which generates OS, the free will choices of $NPMR_N$ residents interact with the beings, objects, and energy of $NPMR_N$ to create and actualize successive $NPMR_N$ states of being, which in turn enables the generation of $NPMR_N$'s present and probable future states. As far as I can tell, the digital-state-flipping-AUM-consciousness-bright-awareness-thing directly controls NPMR's outer loop.

3. How the Probable Reality Surface Changes

As previously discussed, PMR real-time moves on as DELTA-t is successively iterated. Not only can the expectation values of a future probable state be computed, but the rate of change of these projected probabilities everywhere on that surface can also be computed as a function of DELTA-t. Because these calculations have been made for a large number of DELTA-t, the history of how the probable reality surface has actually changed with respect to real-time is now known. This information (sensitivity of our probability functions to perturbations) can be used to help calculate better, more accurate probable realities. In fact this is exactly what has been going on all along. The probable reality surface represents the most likely future possibilities.

As the present consumes the surface at the origin (t = 0), the surface is extended further into the future at the outer perimeter of the disk [t = $\mathbf{M} \cdot$(DELTA-t)]. It might be profitable, though simplistic, to imagine the probable reality surface as a circular plane with t = 0 at the center and with t spreading out (increasing value) radially in all directions at once (see Figure 5-2). As real-time marches on, the plane disappears (moves), one DELTA-t at a time, into the pinhole at the origin while a new ring, DELTA-t wide is added to its outer edge to maintain a constant radius of $\mathbf{M} \cdot$(DELTA-t). The disk is thus made up of $\mathbf{M}$ concentric flat rings, with each ring being one DELTA-t wide.

The pinhole, (more correctly, the mathematical point at t = 0) into which the future probable reality surface is being sucked, represents the present moment. After the present moment, all state vectors are saved. In other words, the present state is defined and subsequently saved to a history file, which contains every previous present state. We will see later how these past (previously actualized) states, captured by saving their present state vectors, remain vital and capable of branching to new potential virtual reality system within TBC's calculation space whenever additional significant input is introduced.

4. Predicting the Future

There will be some peaks on the surface that will have relatively large, stable and growing values. Some of these may occasionally occur far out in time (the future). These peaks and the events they represent or relate to would be good bets if you were a prognosticator. The narrower and taller the peak, the more precise the prediction and the more likely the event represented is to occur. Thus, we have future events that can be predicted with good reliability coexisting compatibly with individual free will. From the PMR point of view, intentionally or unintentionally tapping into this database of the most probable possible future events seems to, but does not actually, support the concept of predestination. Free will is required to convert probable events into actual events within the present moment. All information on probable futures is fully accessible from a larger perspective (if your intrinsic noise level is low enough) at: RWW.NPMRN.OS.PMR/probable-reality-database/specific-event/specific-intent.

5. Group Futures

Future probable reality surfaces for a particular group, activity, or happening can be computed. Specific summations can be taken over all the choices made by sentient beings and all the changes of objects and energy that have, or are projected to have, an impact or influence on a particular group (family, tribe, organization, corporation, nation, culture, planet, fault line slip, endangered species, rain forest, football team, or human race). The specific group's probable reality surface shows only those probable future events that are significant or related to that group. An individual interested in a specific group's probable future can easily filter all interactions for only those that pertain to that particular group through a process that is analogous to submitting a database query function where your intent designs and executes the query. A view of the collected events that are defined and limited by the properties of your query-intent, along with their associated probability values, are available to you through the RWW net.

6. The Probable Future can Change

The rate of change (fluctuations on the surface) of the probability functions for expected events for individuals is much faster than the fluctuations for a large group of individuals. Thus, a nation's future is easier to predict than an individual's (is a more slowly varying and stable surface). The probabilities on the probable-reality surface representing our entire planet change even more slowly, allowing for more accurate prognostication. Think of the probable future of a group or organization as the vector summation of all the probable future components of the individuals that affect that group weighted by their likely significance (impact) on the group.

In general, the larger the system, the more "inertia" it has (the less it can be affected by an individual's free will choices or by small random components within objects and energy), and the more stable and reliably predictable its probable-reality surface becomes. On the RWW net, information about these more clear (larger and more stable signal) future events exhibits a higher signal to noise ratio to everyone and therefore the information (likelihood of some particular event) is more accessible to more people. (Know anybody who claims knowledge of future earth changes? By the hundreds!)

7. Constraining the Number of Required Calculations

The computational burden is not as horrendous as it might seem. Most of the possible choices produce degenerate (the same) results and can be quickly dispensed with. Individuals only have influence or impact on a small subset (that may or may not be significant) of the complete set of interactions and choices. Objects, energy, and people with free will are generally more predictable than you might guess – particularly if you have all the historical data.

Only a relative few individuals at any one time (even in any one year or decade) have the potential to influence or produce major effects as a result of their choices (what they do significantly impacts the choices of many others). Additionally, large subsets of beings, energy, and objects may be functionally independent of each other. For example, earth relevant calculations could proceed as an independent set until **interaction** with specific extraterrestrials (ETs) from elsewhere in our universe occurs. Same for the ETs. Furthermore, there are certain rule-set constraints, such as our PMR laws of physics (things never fall up), which further limit the possibilities.

Despite the mitigating factors of degeneracy, independent sets, and other constraints, computing everything that can happen in the universe and all associated interdependent expectation values (probabilities) is a big job, **but it is finite**. Fortunately, TBC has no problem performing this task using only a small fraction of its overall capacity.

8. Defining Our System (OS) to Include All the Players

An interesting side issue is that of manipulated choice. The manipulation, leading, predisposing, or nudging of PMR awareness by those aware in NPMR$_N$ is another mechanism through which certain probable outcomes are made more likely than others. In other words, another set of interactions that must be taken into account (as part of the OS calculation space input data), are the actions and free will choices made by those extant in NPMR$_N$, but not in PMR, that directly influence or impact the beings in PMR. This interaction affects the state of OS, and is therefore (by definition) a part of OS.

Some of those large, stable, and growing probability peaks exist because they are being encouraged or manipulated by NPMR$_N$ residents who may have much larger perspectives, much better information, a much clearer sense of the future (a better, bigger picture), and a more accessible knowledge base than PMR residents. Consequently, while some peaks (likely events) simply happen of and by themselves, others are guided. Most are a mixture of both.

TBC calculations relevant to our local reality system (OS) must include all beings, objects, and energy in the NPMR$_N$ superset that have an influence upon, or interaction with, our PMR probable-reality surface (not only those beings, objects and energy that exist within our PMR subset). TBC and its software (which can be clever, and does not have to execute a simple brute force approach) are by design thorough and precise in calculating and tracking the facts, possibilities, and probabilities of Our System (OS). OS creates or actualizes its larger reality through the choices of all its interactive beings (embodied or not) and the randomness of all its interactive objects and energy (physical or nonphysical). Changes must abide by the PMR space-time rule-set, the NPMR$_N$ rule-set, the rules of interaction between PMR and NPMR$_N$, and the psi uncertainty principle. Our history (the history of PMR), from a larger perspective, is a subset of the overall history of OS – as European history is a subset of world history.

9. Reality System State Vectors and Our History

During a given real-time increment DELTA-t, beings, objects, and energy may move (or change in some other way) and choices are made to actualize the new present which is contained within the state vector representing that DELTA-t. All potential choices not made remain unactualized potential states (possible realities) and have associated expectation values. The complete state vector of OS containing all actualized and unactualized choices is saved in TBC.

The state vector that defines or represents OS at a given increment of time (DELTA-t) is the total collection of information and data that completely specifies everything that actually did happen and possibly could happen (every significant possibility within that DELTA-t), along with their associated probable-reality surfaces. You will hear more about this later.

Thus, the progression of PMR from one DELTA-t to the next DELTA-t produces or traces a history which is the sum total of all the changes and choices that are actually made or actualized that affect or interact with PMR. This trace becomes an OS history thread representing everything that did happen, or in other words, a sequence of all the states of OS that were actualized during each DELTA-t.

The system is not closed. The system is open; beings, objects and energy can come and go in and out of effective interaction during any DELTA-t. TBC keeps track of, and up with, everything that is significant to (interacts with) OS.

This process and its results define our particular world, our particular history, our particular universe, our particular virtual reality – we who are interacting are all in this together, so to speak. Our choices define, in our view, a collective thread of continuous happening and unfolding generated by beings interacting with each other and with objects and energy.

The OS state vector containing the possibilities and probable reality surfaces not actualized, as well as those that were actualized, is saved at the end of each DELTA-t. For this reason, you can, from an awareness in $NPMR_N$, visit the past, view it, extract information from it (it is on the RWW), and even make changes to it that initiate new calculated arrays of un-actualized past probable realities. We will discuss this in more detail later.

10. History, Still Vital After All These Years

You can interact with the actualized as well as the potential non-actualized past. When you interact with any part of it in such a way as to modify it (introduce a new being, new things, new energy, or a new configuration of old things, or change a significant choice or action), a new set of probable futures is computed that incorporates the changes as new initial conditions. A new set of probable reality calculations can now be progressed, creating a new branch, within the non-actualized past database. The nature of this process is like making a copy of a file or simulation program so that you can play what-ifs with it without disturbing the original.

Any point along the OS timeline, actualized or not, is a potential branch point, but branches do not spontaneously sprout from every point – they occur only when a significant change in the reality state vector is produced by defining a new and unique set of potentialities. If the change creating new initial conditions is trivial as evidenced by no significant change in the future probable reality surfaces for **all** reasonable possibilities (not only the most likely ones), then that branch degenerates back to the initial point of departure. Adding a new electron to the system or changing an irrelevant choice, therefore, does not start a new parallel reality in the what-if calculation space of TBC. More of our choices than you would probably guess are irrelevant in the interactive Big Picture.

In summary, I have described what happens when a change is made to any part or detail of the complete set of everything that could possibly happen, which is computed at the end of each real-time (PMR-time) DELTA-t based on the history of all the beings, objects and energy and on all possible configurations or choices. Because of the small size of DELTA-t, our PMR history appears to be a continuous thread traced by the collective result of the interactions and choices taken, experienced, or actualized. What has not been actualized up to this point has simply been saved. However, both non-actualized past and probable future states remain operationally viable allowing the state vector database to be queried and what-if simulations to be executed by intent.

8

■■■

A Model of Reality and Time Using the Delta-t Loop to Project (Simulate) Everything Significant That Could Possibly Happen in OS

■■■

Let's generalize and broaden our model by looking at the possibility that everything significant that can happen does happen. This is a key concept to understanding the breadth of our multi-dimensional reality, and to appreciating how AUM optimizes the output of its consciousness experiments by collecting data and amassing statistics that describe **all possibilities** simultaneously.

In the previous chapter, I described the complete set of state vectors representing everything that will **most likely** happen in OS. This was computed by incrementing delta-t (simulation time) through **M** consecutive iterations in between each increment of DELTA-t (PMR time). Recall that for each iteration **m** (as **m** progresses from **m** = 1 to **m** = **M**), the delta-t loop converged upon the most probable future state. This was accomplished by evaluating **all** the possible future states in order to determine the most probable one. The most probable future state for that iteration of **m** then becomes part of the set of stored OS probable reality state vectors. Now TBC is going to track and store **every** significant possible future state (and its associated expectation value) that is evaluated for each iteration of **m**, not only the most probable one.

In order to assess **all the significant possibilities,** our understanding of the delta-t loop must be expanded. A more generalized delta-t loop process must now not only compute the most likely future states, but also track **all** (regardless of their likelihood) possible **significant** future states for each iteration **m** = 1, 2, 3,... **M**. Furthermore, each of these possible future states is assigned an expectation value that is a measure of its like-lihood of being actualized. The mechanics and implications of this broad-ened delta-t loop functionality are discussed in detail in the remainder of this chapter, and are illustrated in Figure 5-3.

Before continuing with the description of this new application of the delta-t loop, I want to define the concept of significant states. A signifi-cant state is one that represents some unique, viable, meaningful config-uration of OS, even if it is perhaps somewhat unlikely. Essentially, TBC generates significant states by computing all the permutations and com-binations of all the free will choices, all the potential changes in objects, all the energy state changes, and then eliminates the redundant or insignificant states. All significant states with a probability of actualization above some small arbitrary value are enumerated.

For a given value of the iteration index **m**, the total number of signifi-cant possible future states is not known until after they have been gener-ated. Thus, as the delta-t loop is iterated, there may be a different total number of significant possible (though not necessarily probable) future states for each specific iteration **m**. Recall however that for each specific iteration of **m**, only one of the significant possible future states will even-tually be actualized and take its place on our seemingly continuous OS-PMR history thread. The state that eventually becomes actualized will probably be the one that was previously given the highest probability of being actualized – but not necessarily. The collective free will is free to choose whatever it will; updates and adjustments are made as needed to accommodate the vagaries of free will.

Perhaps the simplest way to think of this generalized process is to imag-ine that a dimension of width has been added to the information recorded during each iteration **m** of the delta-t loop. Look ahead to Figure 5-3: The example given shows parent-child state generation exhibiting geometric growth. During the first iteration of **m** (**m** = 1) there are three significant possible futures states generated (OS_1, OS_2, OS_3), including the one determined to be most probable (double bordered OS_3). TBC tracks and stores all three states associated with the iteration **m** = 1. Here we have chosen the small number three (**M** = 3) to make our visualization easier to grasp and present graphically. In actuality, there are a very large varying number of significant possible future states. Every cir-cle in Figure 5-3 represents a unique state vector of OS.

This newly expanded function of the delta-t loop (tracking all possible states instead of just the most likely ones) represents a generalized larger view of our previous understanding. As such, it is more complicated to

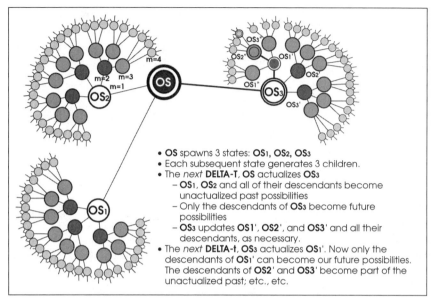

- OS spawns 3 states: OS1, OS2, OS3
- Each subsequent state generates 3 children.
- The *next* **DELTA-T**, OS actualizes OS3
  - OS1, OS2 and all of their descendants become unactualized past possibilities
  - Only the descendants of OS3 become future possibilities
  - OS3 updates OS1', OS2', and OS3' and all their descendants, as necessary.
- The *next* **DELTA-t**, OS3 actualizes OS1'. Now only the descendants of OS1' can become our future possibilities. The descendants of OS2' and OS3' become part of the unactualized past; etc., etc.

Figure 5.3: Generating the Possible States of OS

describe and to follow. Referring to the simple example given in Figure 5-3 may help provide a better understanding. The next step ($m = 2$) of this generalized NPMR_N delta-t loop is to project (simulate) a set of possible (though not necessarily probable) future states for each of the alternative states generated for $m = 1$. That is to say that each significant **possible** future state that is generated during iteration m spawns another complete set of significant possible future states during the next value of m (and so on as m is sequentially stepped to M). For example, in Figure 5-3 **each** nearly solid black state ($m = 2$) generates three medium gray ($m = 3$) states, which each generate three light gray states ($m = 4$).

The result is a geometrically expanding array of significant possible future states originating with the current OS and iterating M generations into the simulated (projected) future – representing a total elapsed time of $M \cdot (\text{DELTA-t})$.

In summary, during iteration $m = 2$, **each** of the previously generated (first generation) alternative states will generate some number of significant possible (second generation) future states of its own. The generalized delta-t loop is then recursively applied to each second-generation alternative state. This process continues until the delta-t loop has projected **all** significant possible future states of OS for $m = 1, 2, 3, ...M$ iterations by simulating (projecting) everything significant that could possibly happen (above a certain level of expectation) during **M** consecutive increments of DELTA-t.

We are no longer working exclusively with what is **most likely** to become actualized and what has previously been actualized (our PMR-OS history). We have now formed a super-set that includes all that, as well as some significant (worth following) states that will not and did not happen. In other words, a larger, broader set of states defining **all significant** possibilities of OS has been formed. Mechanically, this was accomplished by expanding the scope of the delta-t loop to recursively enumerate and determine **all** the **significant** possibilities of OS.

This enumeration and determination of potentially significant state vectors does not need to be accomplished by computational brute force. Given that the Fundamental Process would unquestionably need to create extremely clever evaluative operating systems and software for TBC as it functionally evolved within AUM's consciousness, we can assume a certain efficiency of process is achieved. After all, evolution is the unparalleled master of developing efficient and effective processes within each specific operating environment. For example, such software could be used to remove all the extremely unlikely, insignificant, uninteresting, unproductive, degenerate, duplicative, repetitive, meaningless, and useless states to form a complete set of useful alternate reality state vectors specifying **everything significant** that possibly could happen in OS during the next actual DELTA-t. Recall Topic 4 in Chapter 4 of this book for a short list of overall goals that suggests some of the evaluation criteria this expert system software might use to make decisions. Remember, the evaluative processes do not have to be perfect – the final results need only be functionally adequate and statistically meaningful – perfect calculations and processes are never required.

TBC calculates the probability that each projected possible OS state vector might be actualized by the free will choices and changes in objects and energy that will be made during the next actual increment of DELTA-t. The one that is most likely to be actualized represents the first point ($\mathbf{m} = 1$) on the future probable reality surface of OS that we discussed in the previous chapter. In the example shown in Figure 5-3, the states that will eventually be actualized are double bordered. OS_3 most likely, but not necessarily, represents the first ($\mathbf{m} = 1$) flat ring on OS's **most probable** future reality surface. (Reference Figure 5-2 located in Chapter 7 at the end of Topic 3 in this book.) OS_2 and OS_1 are also $\mathbf{m} = 1$ states but remain unactualized – the choices they represent were not chosen by the collected free will actions of the sentient beings in OS during that actual DELTA-t.

The next pass ($\mathbf{m}$ = 2: solid black circles) through this generalized OS DELTA-t simulator will allow **each** of the possible $\mathbf{m}$ = 1 states (both likely and unlikely) to likewise generate all the possible significant states that could be generated from the initial conditions that this particular state vector represents. Again, the probabilities of actualization are computed for **every** state vector generated. For example, only one state generated by OS_3 can be most probable and take its place on the most probable future reality surface of OS_3. Also only one state (depicted by double bordered $OS_{1'}$ in Figure 5-3) generated by OS_3 will be actualized by the free will of the sentient beings within OS_3. This process, repeated $\mathbf{M}$ times (once for each value of $\mathbf{m}$) gets to be a mind full. I am afraid that we will need to resort to a generalized subscript notation to keep this mental picture focused.

Let's take it from the top utilizing subscripts to form a generalized description of this process. Each alternate reality state vector, differentiated by the index $\mathbf{i}$, represents the state vector defining OS_i. The subscript $\mathbf{i}$ keeps track of as many unique state vectors ($\mathbf{i}$ = 1, 2, 3, ...) as there are unique arrangements of sentient choices and other variables (objects, position, or energy). These OS_i state vectors constitute parallel, possible, or potential future realities of OS or from a PMR-centric view, parallel, possible, or **potential** future universes. Sometimes travelers in $NPMR_N$ get into these parallel realities (such as the never-to-be-actualized solid dark (m = 2) or medium gray (m =3) circles attached to OS_1 or OS_2 – or the could-be-actualized light gray (m = 4) outermost circles attached to $OS_{3''}$), and fail to realize they represent reality states that were or are merely possible and not necessarily probable. A measure of each state's probability of being actualized is available, but needs to be accessed with a separate intent. In other words, the probability of actualization does not automatically come integrated with the experience of the reality – you have to ask a separate question and be precise with your initial intent.

Each of the alternate reality state vectors described above becomes the starting point for another. Everything significant that could possibly happen is computed based on the unique permutations and combinations of all the possible states of objects, energy, and the free will choices of beings originating from the particular initial conditions of each particular alternate reality state vector.

Thus, parent OS_i (first generation) state vector possibilities spawn new child $OS_{i'}$ state vectors (second generation), which in turn spawns yet a new generation of child $OS_{i''}$ state vectors (third generation). This progression continues so on and so forth, until one has progressed this family tree of possible states (all offspring of the original OS and all computed during the single time increment DELTA-t) through **M** generations. Remember, **M** is an arbitrarily large but finite integer.

Every alternate state vector (every circle in Figure 5-3) can generate its own probable reality surface of expectation values by tracing the states that are most probable from generation to generation of its descendants. (Note: **M** is finite because this is a **real** process generating the real reality that we presently live in. This does not represent an imaginary or theoretical process – it is a practical **model** of how the larger reality operates.)

In this way, the number of unique and useful alternate reality system state vectors grows (removing all useless and redundant states) until we arrive at a complete set of alternate reality system state vectors representing everything that could uniquely and usefully (significantly) happen. All the state vectors that result from this progression have been derived (originated) from the OS state vector during this present DELTA-t (our present moment).

During the next DELTA-t, one (and only one) of these possible states (first generation OS_i) becomes actualized (through our free will choices and the changing objects and energy) as our next present moment. The descendants of that state (the OS_i that was actualized) become unactualized **future** possibilities, while the descendants of all the other non-actualized OS_i (a much larger group) become unactualized **past** possibilities. TBC saves and stores everything.

The unactualized future possibilities have a finite chance of being actualized at some time in the future, while the unactualized past possibilities can now never be actualized by free will choices within OS. Now integrate this picture with the one described in the previous chapter. If, from the set of simulated unactualized future possibilities you trace the single most likely state to be actualized within each of the **M** generations, you would have defined the probable reality surface for OS that was defined in Chapter 7 of this book.

The word "actualized," as it is used here, refers to what actually happened or actually took place from our perspective – the perspective of OS. States are actualized and reality is created in the present moment. For us, it is created DELTA-t by DELTA-t – one increment (fundamental time quantum of PMR) at a time. The history of OS is the sequential record of the actualized present moments of OS.

Because time is quantized, and TBC has a good memory, both the actualized and unactualized states (state vectors) can be saved. Every saved state vector is as complete, vital, and capable of generating new states as any other saved state vector within TBC. The set of state vectors within the group called unactualized past possibilities are not dead states; they are simply dormant states. They are as alive and vital as any – they have simply not been actualized or chosen by the free will choices and changes of objects and energy that define the dynamic history thread of Our System of reality.

▶ A short aside is in order here. I can hear you wondering:

"Granted, every state vector is theoretically capable of generating new states, but why would an unactualized state do this?"

You are absolutely correct: It wouldn't change spontaneously. It would simply sit there with all its possibilities laid out for **M** generations, unless something changed in its defining choice-set. For example, a sentient being could travel back through history to that particular state vector and alter something significant, thus modifying that state vector and all its descendants. If the change represented one of the possible choices previously considered (highly likely), no new calculations are necessary, otherwise a new branch is generated and a new larger set of possibilities would be created.

However, even if a new array were generated, once all its possibilities were filled out it would simply sit there until additional unique significant changes were introduced. There is no need to continue making calculations on unactualized states of a particular OS. Unactualized states do not require much updating – unless somebody with free will is introducing new significant initial conditions and creating new branches within the old set of possibilities. They simply sit there as a mostly static complete array (database) of the possibilities and retain the **potential** to branch (calculate new possibilities) if new initial conditions are introduced.

This arrangement (allowing for unique input while maintaining an exhaustive database of possibilities) enables the running of what-if analysis to ascertain the impact of having made specific choices. This type of analysis is often used as an aid to help certain sentient beings that are between physical manifestations in PMR to understand the implications of previous choices and overcome personal belief systems. Such analysis is a typical part of the planning process for more aware beings trying to learn as much as possible from their past experiences before initiating another PMR experience.

For those who do not understand the larger reality well enough or do not have the necessary control, others typically guide this process for them. This analysis capability is generally available to any $NPMR_N$ or PMR being who is sufficiently aware and in control of their mental faculties and intent within $NPMR_N$. ◀

Now that DELTA-t has incremented and an OS_i state has been actualized as the current OS state, the second generation $OS_{i'}$, that are children of the **actualized** OS_i state, become first generation possibilities to the present actualized moment. Again, **M** generations beyond the present state are computed for **all** states (actualized and unactualized) that contain significant possibilities. And so on, and so forth, this process marches on, generating and computing potential reality-system state vectors describing everything significant that might happen, along with everything significant that might have happened (but didn't, from our point of view). TBC saves every state vector, its genealogy, and its likelihood or probability (relative to its siblings) of being actualized by its parent.

The past of OS is represented by a particular solid thread connecting all our past **actualized** states as it meanders through the matrix of all past possibilities. Our perceived past or history can also be described as a specific sequenced subset (previously actualized states) of the all-past-states database. Likewise, our probable future is represented by a dashed thread snaking through a vastly smaller database of future possible states, picking out only the states with the highest likelihood of actualization, as it moves sequentially from generation to generation. This future thread represents the most probable reality or probable future surface of OS (see Topics 1 and 8 in Chapter 7 of this book).

We have described and generated a set of state vectors representing everything significant that can happen (including everything significant that might have happened and everything significant that might happen yet) through **M** generations beyond the original common ancestor OS. All this is calculated between each DELTA-t. Because this concept is complex, let us summarize quickly before continuing.

Previously, we developed probable reality surfaces for **M** sequential simulated increments of DELTA-t. These probable reality surfaces only described **everything most likely to happen**. Now, we have broadened that concept by describing **everything significant that could happen**. The process starts with OS at a particular DELTA-t and projects (simulates) **M** generations of **possible** future significant states of OS. This is accomplished between successive **actual DELTA-t** increments (real-time is standing still in OS). It is accomplished by incrementing the $NPMR_N$ delta-t loop, which, at each iteration **m**, generates **all** the significant possibilities (the OS_i) for **each** of the OS alternative states previously defined. This delta-t process continues through **M** iterations, progressing and expanding to project or simulate **everything significant that could possibly happen** during the next **M** iterations of DELTA-t.

The next **actual DELTA-t** (real-time in OS moves forward one increment), one and only one of the OS_i states, is actualized to become our present moment. The actualization of only one state leaves a large set of unactualized past possibilities. Every state not connected upstream to our newly actualized present state becomes an unactualized past possibility. In other words, only those relatively few states that are descended from the just actualized (our new present) state now make up our future possibilities. TBC always maintains a calculation space of **M** generations beyond the present. (We will generalize the concept of **M** later but it will serve us well in the meantime to think of it as a fixed integer.) As this process continues, redundant states among the unactualized past possibilities are collapsed. Entire branches of this family tree may cease to expand for lack of further significant unique possibilities.

The initial massive calculation (running the delta-t loop to generate every significant possible future state through **M** generations) must be done only once (say during the first increment – the beginning of time for OS). Other than a few relatively minor adjustments that may need to be applied to the previously generated states (allowing for unforeseen changes in initial conditions and imperfections in TBC's evaluative and predictive software), all that remains is the creation of the newest generation of children states.

Every actualized reality system state vector, flourishing and evolving within its own dimension, represents a **dynamic open** (entities and objects can come and go) reality with an active copy of you and everyone else (including all the objects and energy) it inherited from its parent (along with all the pending potential choices, interactions, and conditions).

It may be helpful here to point out that dimension is to TBC as a line on a sheet of paper is to us. Or better yet, as the text-line on a computer screen is to us – simply press the enter key to get a new one. Those analogies are not perfect. Perhaps a better one would be that dimension is to TBC as a saved file in our computer is to us. You get the idea. TBC spins off a new computationally alive dimension within Our System's multidimensional reality for every uniquely significant reality system state vector it generates.

In a bigger picture, each dimensioned local reality (the various PMR_k for example) describes a diverging, branching, set of uniquely dimensioned potential worlds. Think of saved files that may contain sub-files – folders within folders – with each folder or sub-file containing an executing piece of the overall simulation. Each reality exists within a unique dimension, folder, or memory space within TBC. All these realities existing within their various dimensions or dynamic folders are computationally alive (can be modified) subsets of a larger simulation, expanding into their potential futures by the beat of their **own** time artificially constructed or simulated by successive increments of DELTA-t_k. OS is one of those local realities – the one that we sentient beings in OS have collectively chosen to actualize. I will discuss this subject again from a slightly different viewpoint in Topic 3, Chapter 11 of this book where we will again contemplate an Even Bigger Computer (EBC) and multiple PMR_k.

We have thus constructed a process to support everything significant that can happen, in fact, does happen – at least in TBC calculation space. Nevertheless, everything that can happen is not actualized. If, in the rare instance (allowing for imperfection in TBC's software) where the state that is actualized is not (to a significant degree) one of the previously generated OS_i, then it is simply added to the set of OS_i.

Although TBC's software can be exceptionally clever and efficient, it does not have to be perfect. Perfect processes, like infinite processes, are unnecessary to the development of this model. We are talking about real processes here, processes that are imperfect and finite. There are a finite number of beings, objects, and energy states among objects, and each of these have a finite number of choices and ways to change. All the significant permutations and combinations of all the possibilities through all **M** generations is probably an extremely large number (especially from our PMR perspective), but it is finite and consumes only a tiny fraction of the capacity of an apparently infinite (but actually finite) AUM.

9

■■■

A Model of Reality and Time
Viable Alternate Realities
and Histories

■■■

The previously described process of progressing OS through **M** generations beyond the present (in order to represent everything significant
that can happen) began to include PMR with the initiation of the Big
Digital Bang, or the Big Set of Initial Conditions, or the Big Start of the
Simulation. Our scientists use the word "Big" because we are such a tiny
part of the entire universe. However in a bigger picture, our physical universe is neither big nor exclusive. In fact, it is every bit as small and insignificant from the Big Picture view as it is grandly immense from our little picture (PMR) view. Nevertheless, "Big Bang" is a catchy and likable term
even if it is not that big and even if the bang is only a digital one in calculation-space within the space-time simulation section of TBC. OS has incremented its way forward in time within TBC ever since the time loop driving the Big Bang digital-mind simulation started incrementing our PMR
forward by applying the space-time rule-set to the given initial conditions.

When the state of PMR (within the simulation) was mostly rapidly
changing matter and energy, alternative space-time realities were generated. Some were produced by sampling over the randomness (choices)
within material and energetic processes. As always, the Fundamental
Process was in the driver's seat; all possible states were generated but only
those universes supporting PMRs that were uniquely useful, productive,
or significant were propagated forward. One of them became our universe while others evolved, in their own dimensions (sub-sets of TBC), to
represent some of the other PMRs mentioned earlier (see Chapter 4 in
this book).

Nothing could be more elegant or efficient than to initiate the virtual material part of AUM's continuing experiment in consciousness, than beginning with a huge virtual space-time energy (remember $E = mc^2$ or equivalently, $m = E/c^2$) at a point (or within a small volume) and... Bang! Or rather, Big Bang! Wow, look at that stuff go (evolve) – one DELTA-t at a time – all according to the space-time rule-set. Our scientists have some simulations like that, but I am sure they are not as good as TBC's. The previous sentence should not be construed to denigrate our brilliant, bushy-headed scientists, but is simply attributable to the fact that TBC has a much better computational capacity and throughput as well as the **complete** space-time rule-set.

Recalling that simulation time can run much slower or faster than real-time, and that any result or intermediary state may be modified, saved, or deleted, gives us an appreciation of the control AUM has over the eventual development of our local PMR reality and the evolution of the space-time rule-set used to define allowed interactions (within this book, see Chapter 5 and Topic 2 in Chapter 7). AUM may have initiated, run, and rerun this simulation process many times before all the initial conditions, parameters, rule-sets, and relationships had evolved to the point that the results met all the specifications of a top-notch learning laboratory capable of effectively supporting the consciousness cycle. This is how AUM and TBC generate the PMR virtual reality set that we call home – likewise, for all the space-time reality sets that other sentient beings call home.

When a subset of sentient beings within $NPMR_N$ were able to use (inhabit) the evolving virtual physical reality we call PMR profitably, their free will choices driving learning, growth, physical evolution, and spiritual evolution became interactive with the virtual objects and energy of PMR as well as with each other. These interactions generated the OS probable realities and alternate reality state vectors that were the predecessors of our present OS. Some of the sentient beings in $NPMR_N$ that existed before our PMR's digital Big Bang were a part of OS by virtue of their involvement in planning and executing OS's origins – the seemingly mystical beginnings of our universe – yet mystical only from a PMR perspective.

A still living and still potent history of OS (actualized and unactualized) continues to exist in TBC where any saved state is able to calculate or simulate more children if something unique and significant is added or changed. This easily animated living history is available to us from $NPMR_N$. For example, any state vector that lies on our history thread, regardless of where it is located on the thread, is available not only for inspection but also for a what-if tour of the probabilities. The accumulated database of everything that could have possibly happened since the PMR virtual reality was created provides a huge resource for data mining.

There are many unactualized states that can be strung together into continuous threads that represent significant choices that could have been made differently; such traces represent an unactualized history that is different from ours. Any number of unactualized history threads may share a common state with our actualized OS history at some particular DELTA-t, but subsequently have gone their separate ways. These unactualized and usually less probable history threads represent a particular sequence of events that did not happen. Nevertheless, the study of such what-if world-lines or sequential traces through the unactualized state vector database can reveal the long term impact of decisions, choices and intents, an excellent educational and evaluative tool.

Recall that each state vector has an associated expectation value that properly fixes its likelihood of happening given the initial conditions of the parent. One can sequence or thread his or her way through unactualized consecutive reality states (past or probable future) that are OS derivatives in a huge multitude of ways that are intentionally controllable and definable only by a steady, low-noise, focused aware consciousness.

These sequences of related states are (from our view) called parallel, divergent, or alternate realities. These alternate realities are computationally viable in TBC and are populated by mathematical representations (statistical simulations) of each sentient player as well as mathematical representations of the objects and energy. It is relatively easy for a novice explorer of the RWW network to get lost or confused in these parallel worlds. The explorer comes back with information that seemed to be correct and clear at the time, however, later analysis often indicates that paranormally derived information does not make sense, has little PMR value, or is shown to be false or inconsistent by subsequent events or information within PMR. It is easy to end up wandering unknowingly in the unactualized data matrix of TBC because it (the interactions and the experience) appears as real as any experience can be. The experience of an unactualized computational reality is like seeing a movie where you are simultaneously an actor (exercising free will to drive the story line) as well as a member of the audience. An unintentional experience of an unactualized computational reality is indistinguishable from the experience you are having now – except that it disappears when you shift your focus back to PMR (as PMR tends to disappear when your awareness becomes preoccupied with a mantra, a problem, entertainment, or befuddled by drugs).

The set of state vectors comprising the history thread of OS, the OS present, and the set of OS probable futures are no more or less real or dynamic than the set of state vectors that comprise the unactualized past. All are of equal reality and validity. All share the same properties and are similar data types within TBC. The only difference is that some were actualized by our choices while others were not. The only difference is us – what our individual quality expressed as a free will intent actually did. The set of actualized OS state vectors represents the collective quality of our consciousness within OS, expressed as a unique path through the possibilities.

Previously, I have referred to choices and changes in objects and energy as drivers of actualization. The possibilities that may be actualized are derived from the possible free will choices of sentient beings, the constraints of the space-time rule-set, as well as from the randomness associated with objects and energy (material movement, changes, interactions). Physical randomness and the constraints of the space-time rule-set drive the actualization of natural events such as earthquakes or thunderstorms. Physical changes may be expressed as the choices that inanimate objects and energy make.

In that sense, objects and energy make choices as they evolve toward minimum energy states along the path of least resistance. Objects and energy must make their choices in strict obedience to the space-time rule-set – the consistency of space-time physics is important to the usefulness of PMR. These choices are not the moral choices of a free will and do not reflect the quality of consciousness of the chooser. To avoid confusion, let's call the results of physical or natural randomness (such as radioactive decay) rule-driven possibilities, as opposed to the choice-driven or free will driven possibilities that conscious, aware, sentient entities sometimes make.

Sentient beings may contain small random components within their intent, and larger random components within their perception, interpretation, and reaction to their internal and external environments. Random components play a part in what sentient beings experience, and how they react to, and interact with, that experience. Consider the random components influencing experience as spice, not the main ingredients. Randomness occasionally dominates the flavor of existence for some entities some of the time (usually short term), however, the quality of your choices are a much bigger driver of eventual long-term outcomes than randomness.

On the up-side, randomness helps to deliver an interesting and ever changing array of experiential opportunities to which we interactively apply our free will intent at whatever level of quality we have thus far generated.

It is these experiences, these opportunities with their sometimes-random components that enable us to evolve our consciousness. When free will meets an opportunity to interact with our internal or external environments, consciousness has the opportunity to grow, stagnate, or degenerate. Do you see why a virtual physical PMR-type learning lab is so useful? Straightforward interactive opportunities with clear results and feedback abound everywhere we focus our attention in PMR. PMR is constrained to be a highly interactive experience at the most basic level of relationship. Interacting with the other PMR players (an interaction of free wills) is the main thing we do here in PMR: This interaction is the basis of our opportunity to evolve the quality of our consciousness.

The set of possibilities that may be actualized as a result of many individual actions taken by a group such as a club or organization (or perhaps a government) are defined by a superposition of all the free will choices of all the sentient beings in OS that have some influence or impact on the actions of that organization. Thus, we also describe group choices as choice-driven possibilities. Recall that a motivation and intent that has large random components represent a less developed consciousness with large entropy. This is true of group consciousness as well as individual consciousness.

Possible events, with any value of probability, may be primarily rule driven, primarily choice driven, or a combination of both. Thus, for example, some relatively clear (large signal to noise ratio) future events (see Chapters 3 and 7 in this book), such as potential coming earth changes, gain their strong signals or large stable and growing probability values (densities) from an interactive mix of rule-driven and choice-driven probability calculations.

From Chapter 7 in this book, recall that the probabilities of actualization, calculated for each successive value of m, define the probable reality surfaces. Also recall that peaks or lumps on the probable reality surface represent the expectation value of a particular event. Do you see how choice-driven and rule-driven actualization creates uncertainty in the expectation values of probable future events? Do you also see that a dynamically evolving free will that is bound to directly express the true quality of its consciousness, along with ubiquitous random components that are typically small and short-term, conspire to maintain a rich mixture of uncertain yet personally focused opportunities within PMR?

Also recall that it is uncertainty, according to the psi uncertainty principle, that allows good planning and manipulations from $NPMR_N$ to influence PMR happenings without being obvious – without stepping outside the space-time rule-set and PMR causality. Consider the natural uncertainty and small random components modeled within the digital consciousness system as the lubricant that helps make the system work.

▶ Let us take a break for a minute in the form of a short aside to police-up some ideas and concepts that fell on the floor while we were explaining the mechanics of reality system state vector generation, propagation, and uncertainty.

It is worth reiterating at this point that there are similar consciousness and physical-matter reality systems working through similar evolutionary process in other space-time PMRs within $NPMR_N$. These realities can be very different from our PMR and exist independently of OS. TBC can be thought of as representing a dedicated server (or calculation space allocated within a larger AUM mainframe process) for the PMR_k within $NPMR_N$. All PMR_k are part of (accessible through) the same NPMR communications net. All are available on the RWW for inspection and participation.

Another point worth mentioning is that the clever evaluative software that defines "significant" by filtering out non-productive, insignificant, redundant, meaningless, or useless reality states does not need to be any more mystical than our artificial intelligence or expert systems software. Like its PMR cousins, it utilizes evaluative criteria, pattern recognition, history files, statistics, and predictive algorithms. Its accuracy is dependent upon an extremely detailed and unusually complete knowledge base.

I have evoked (assumed) nothing fundamentally new or spooky here – only bigger, faster, better. We humans have a tendency to see ourselves with inflated significance. There are perhaps many fewer significant states than you might assume at first glance, making the calculation problem somewhat less monstrous in volume.

Please make note of the fact that thus far, I have not evoked, nor will I evoke, either perfect or infinite processes. OS contains finite numbers of beings and objects, with finite **significant** choices and finite **significant** random events that impact, influence, or interact within a finite universe of objects and energy capable of moving or changing in a finite number of **significant** ways. Thus, though it may seem overwhelmingly large, there are a **finite** number of unactualized past and future OS reality-system state vectors. Recall from an earlier discussion that non-interactive subsets of our larger physical and nonphysical realities can be handled separately. We only have to include that part of $NPMR_S$ and our physical universe that is interactive with our OS's super set of everything that can happen in order to fill out our OS data matrix (see Topic 8 in Chapter 7 of this book.)

Some may think that the data storage requirements and processing requirements are too large to be workable. If you believe that, it is because your vision of what is possible is stuck in the PMR of the twentieth century. To an apparently infinite, highly evolved, aware digital consciousness that employs processing speeds and storage capacity trillions upon trillions upon trillions of orders of magnitude greater than what you could ever imagine in your wildest theoretical dreams, the computational burden is almost trivial. The computational requirements are significant, but they are also finite and well within the capacity of TBC.

On the other hand, you might believe that the mechanics of generating, storing, and progressing OS state vectors as described above is a mystical or supernatural process. It might seem that way to some, but remember what we learned in Chapters18 and 20 of Book 1 – that what appears to be mystical is relative to your experience, and dependant on your perspective. From the perspective of *My Big TOE,* it appears to be a straightforward bookkeeping and computer science application focused on a relatively small (about the size of a petri dish) and relatively simple (like raising guppies in an aquarium) problem. ◀

10

■■■

A Model of Reality and Time
Multiple Copies of You –
Creating Your Reality

■■■

Previously, I defined everything significant that could have happened or that might yet happen. Let us now focus on a piece of our history thread that contains you, as a sentient being, in it. From any particular state that contains your existence, a multitude of dependent child states are generated, which in turn have children that have children through **M** generations. The phrase "everything that can happen does happen" implies that each of the possible representations of you – each virtual you – contained within each **possible unactualized** OS state vector represents the array of possible choices you **could** make at any particular DELTA-t.

You are the entity that made the free will choices you made. There are representations (models) of you that populate all the possibilities that you could have made but didn't within the unactualized past. There are also models of you populating the unactualized possible future states. You, the evolving sentient unit of individuated consciousness, exist only in the present as you make free will choices that actualize one possibility over another and thereby modify the quality of your consciousness. The models of you we are referring to are simply an enumeration of all the possible choices you could have made, or could yet make, with an assessment of the probability that you would actualize each choice. Thus, the model of you is simply a probabilistic estimation of the significant choices you are likely to make under each of the unique circumstances defined within each state vector. This model of you is updated and improved with each set of choices that your conscious free will intent actualizes. Your model represents your quality – it is the result of you – the result of every thought, feeling, desire, intent, choice, and action you have ever made.

Although this simulated or virtual you makes all the same choices you are likely to make in a given situation, it is incapable of learning and changing its representation of you. It is not making free will choices. The replicated you that exists within every unactualized (past and future) state is merely a statistical representation of all the choices you could possibly make and the likelihood (probability) that you would make each one. Thus, TBC populates **all** alternate states with a probabilistic model of you that knows (from your quality and from your history) the likelihood of your making each possible choice (given your past choices and the current array of options). The virtual you is a reasonably accurate simulation or projection of the actual you. (Keep in mind that the actual you we are talking about is you as an individuated unit of consciousness, not you as a PMR body). Think of it as a duplicate of you, a representation of you, **without** the ability to choose by exercising the quality of a freely willed consciousness.

Each alternate or replicated you that inhabits every saved state vector (including the ones you have previously actualized) is actually a representation (predictive model) of your primary energy in $NPMR_N$. Each virtual you represents the likelihood of you making the given significant choices according to the statistics and probability functions that currently model the quality of your consciousness. Though this model of you is an accurate high-fidelity model, it is only a model. It does not represent a sentient consciousness with free will. It is not expressing your intent and is not directly helping or hurting your effort to increase the quality of your consciousness.

The what-if scenarios (divergent reality branches) that you can access in the unactualized past data matrix, for example, are populated exclusively by these modeled individuals who will interact with you (the new inputs you create) according to their own modeled behavior. The adventures or experiences you may have in these or other parallel realities are as real as what you are experiencing now. They are run in what appears to you to be your real-time, are typically not saved, but can be regenerated anytime. Think of it as querying a multidimensional database with your intent where the result of the query is a movie that you both act in and watch.

It is possible (though unlikely) that your consciousness may be integrated with or inhabit more than one free will motivated choice-making entity at the same time. Because whatever arrangement best optimizes your growth potential can generally be implemented, you may exhibit a multiplicity of sentient being; nevertheless this arrangement is not often put to use. Because of the strong coupling between lessons learned from previous physical experiences and probable success with the present physical experience, it is usually a better strategy to plan and execute these learning experiences serially instead of in parallel. Parallel space-time (physical) projections may be in the same PMR at the same time or be scattered among any of the PMR_k. The more developed the consciousness, the more easily it can handle complex arrangements.

Your totality is the sum of all of your projected consciousness fragments that have ever exercised free will. Your primary consciousness energy, sometimes called the over-soul (where the results of your efforts are accumulated) remains always conscious in $NPMR_N$. Think of the over-soul as your main personal data folder. In general, here is how it works: Individual subsets of your sentient (free will possessing) being or consciousness-energy are projected into various frames of reference (dimensions or realities) where their interaction with the challenges and opportunities that they find there produces a change in the quality of your overall consciousness.

The fragment of you (who you think you are) in this PMR may be no more real, special, significant, or successful than other free will expressing fragments of you that have been, are, or will be spread around in various realities (past, present, or future).

Your present (in this reality) personal identity or awareness (the fragment that is currently the brilliant, good-looking, and lovable being that you know you are deep down inside) may be the grandest of the bunch – or it could be the worst, or somewhere in between. Your personal identity is simply the fragment of consciousness (entity) that has made all the choices you have made in conjunction with all the people and objects with whom you have interacted. That statement is also true for all the other past, present, and future free willed projections or fragments of you. Though your over-soul is immortal (disregarding a few rare exceptions), your **present** personal identity will only persist as long as your over-soul finds it profitable to maintain it. The Fundamental Process urges the over-soul to maintain and progress only what is profitable.

Some people refer to their past fragments projected into the PMR reference frame as past lives. That is a good descriptive term, but carries a PMR-only connotation that is too small to fit the bigger picture of all the potential sentient fragments (physical within any of the PMR_k and non-physical within any of the $NPMR_n$) that your over-soul might contain. On the other hand, many sentient entities prefer to specialize in one, or sometimes a few, similar local realities in order to optimize their learning efficiency by narrowing their focus. Thus, an individual might specialize in learning within the context of OS, for much the same reason that a physician might specialize in dermatology. Most entities initially specialize in a single reality system, eventually broadening their experience-base as they develop the quality of their consciousness.

It is possible, though somewhat unlikely, that you have more than one fragment (sentient being belonging to your over-soul) existing in the same PMR at the same time, but you do not need to worry about competition among the various fragments for energy. Such energy is abundant in a digital consciousness reality – from our view it appears to be infinite.

Think about it: The total energy consumed by hundreds of thousands of players in a large war game is nothing more than organization, rules of interaction, goals, memory, and digital processing power. Our concept of energy as fuel (a limited animator of action) is a reflection of our specific space-time rule-set and does not apply to the larger reality. In virtual digital realities, virtual energy fuels the virtual action. There is unlimited energy awaiting your command in NPMR.

Your ability to apply energy to PMR from NPMR (induce paranormal events) by focusing your intent may be limited by your beliefs, ignorance, access privileges, and the psi uncertainty principle, but it is never limited by an unavailability of basic energy. Light workers (a term among New Agers for those who have learned to manipulate consciousness energy between $NPMR_N$ and PMR) never run out of light – an endless supply is always available. If you know how, you can affect a virtual reality from the outside by applying virtual energy (modifying expectation values by intent), but only in accordance with the rules (such as the psi uncertainty principle) of the next larger (parent) reality. To affect a virtual reality from the inside, you must work within the defining rule-set (like putting gas in your tank).

Each fragment projected (in serial or parallel existences) by your over-soul is given as much energy and support as it can profitably use to maximize its learning opportunities. Situations, conditions, and environments are often chosen or planned to provide the kind and type of opportunities that are needed most or that will most effectively improve the whole.

Do not misunderstand me and immediately jump to the conclusion that you are the CEO and chairman of the board of your over-soul. Think of yourself more as a member of a team. You may be on a specific mission to accomplish a specific task that has to do with your personal growth and perhaps the growth of others, or your mission may be non-specific, but more importantly you are adding to the growth of the whole of you while you are focused on this particular PMR experience.

The proper (most productive) perspective is that you are here to develop the quality of consciousness of the fragment you presently represent, not as an agent of your over-soul. The best thing you can do for the whole is to improve yourself by effectively utilizing the opportunities you have. It is that simple. An over-soul that successfully lowers its entropy contributes that benefit to the entire consciousness system.

Thinking that, in your case, a mistake **must** have been made and that your opportunities are more difficult, less fruitful, or contain less potential than they should, or that others have not done their part, or that you are not getting enough help, is a serious mistake. If you think that this might be the case, you don't understand how things work. Trust me; you have everything you need to succeed and the free will to make success happen. You are not in a disadvantaged situation that has been imposed upon you from the outside. If you believe that you are in a disadvantaged situation, you are indeed in a disadvantaged situation, but one created by your beliefs, fears and ego – a situation that only you can change. The success that I am referring to is the success of improving the quality of your consciousness, not making lots of money in the stock market.

You have access to all the quality and understanding that belongs to the whole. If other fragments (in serial or parallel existences) of your fundamental energy make great leaps forward or backward, the quality of your personal fragment of awareness is immediately affected. Great leaps in either direction do occasionally happen, but do not worry too much about the down side. Typically, a fragment of your fundamental energy changes the quality of its consciousness by only very small steps and not by great leaps – that fact is a two edged sword.

For the most part, personal growth, the evolution of your consciousness, is a slow and steady process that cannot be easily hurried or advanced by taking short cuts. The various individual fragments (in serial or parallel existences) of your over-soul are all independent initiators of free will choices.

The individual specific experiences of the various fragments of awareness are kept more or less separate (filed in their own folder within the over-soul folder so to speak) and do not, for the most part, become shared experience. However, the spiritual growth resulting from those experiences is immediately available and shared. You can access (and sometimes interact with) the experiences of the various individual fragments of your over-soul after becoming sentient and in control of your energy within $NPMR_N$. This remains true even if the fragments are not concurrent because all reality states are saved in TBC and remain potentially viable.

Keep in mind that your personal awareness fragment represents only a tiny portion of the free will choices and changes in material and energy that define a present PMR OS state at the end of some DELTA-t increment. Your local reality is a shared reality that represents a vector sum of all the free will choices of all the interacting players. How the virtual ball bounces and the virtual cookie crumbles is the result of a shared effort. All the sentient entities existing upon the earth (Team Earth) are in a collective dance of creative interaction. We get to live with what we create from the opportunities we have. Each individual is an important part of, and affects, the whole. There is no way to cheat others without cheating yourself. Team Earth succeeds or fails together.

Recall that probable futures were generated based on the calculated probable choices of the virtual you (a simulated you). Free will choices were subsequently made which caused one of those probable futures to be actualized. Keep in mind that the things that did not happen (were not actualized) became part of the set of state vectors that define the un-actualized past possibilities. The data within TBC defines what could have been and what is, as well as the part you played in generating that difference.

The choices you make, as well as the possible choices you chose not to make, remain part of the living viable record within the memory (mind) of TBC. All information remains accessible indefinitely on the net within the thought-space or mind-space of $NPMR_N$ where TBC resides. The same is true for all fragments of you. All the information is there to be utilized to maximize the learning and growth of the quality of your consciousness. (Remember that most embarrassing moment of yours – the low point in your quality of being – it's all there, every last minute detail, everything you said, did, and thought! There are no secrets.) This school has one bodacious library! You simply need to know how to apply (yourself) for a card.

The concept of everything that can happen does happen represents an impressive array of information. The tricky part, common to accessing any huge information source, is to find the particular data you want. Knowing what is available and how it is categorized is crucial to developing the skills to access selected data efficiently. Over the centuries, many people have figured out how to tap into a portion of the available database. In general, the smaller your reality, and the less you understand the Big Picture, the easier it is to misinterpret what you find.

Let us peek into the OS file folder and see what data are in there. Thus far, we have discussed the computationally viable states of OS that lie on our collectively actualized history thread as well as the unactualized past states that represent all the possible significant choices you and everybody else could have made (but didn't), and the unactualized future states that represent that set of collective choices that may yet be made. All this information is available for you to experience or to study. The data are not volatile, and the database remains always available. Everyone in OS, physical or nonphysical, participates in generating the OS database.

Others can access your data (every intention, feeling, or thought you have ever had), but there are rules, and only those who have learned how can do so with full awareness. It is not likely that this information will be used for anything other than to help you grow up. However, if you break a rule or get pulled in before a judge, every detail will be scanned to determine the truth of the matter. It is impossible to hide or bluff. Everything is there. Everything! Yes, even that!

The unactualized past is not only recorded, but is alive and kicking in the form of an interactive digital simulation where every player is modeled by a set of expectation values relevant to the possible significant choices. The unactualized past, as well as the states on our history thread, continue indefinitely within the memory of TBC and maintain their interactive potential as unique simulations that are executed according to TBC's statistical models.

The unactualized future states work much the same way except that some of the time (for some individuals under given circumstances), access to certain files is denied. Access is typically denied when the information sought would decrease the probability that an individual will improve the quality of his or her consciousness. Access limitations to the probable-future information are applied for the same reason that we protect small children from hazards (such as loaded guns, dangerous animals, or toxic household chemicals) they are ill equipped to handle.

Many, if not most, people do access some of the data that exist in these probable realities. We call the results of these vaguely intentional queries our intuition. Some people are better than others at accessing the data that are available to their intuition. A developed intuition is a developed awareness of how to purposely access specific data residing in the probable reality and actualized historic databases. Some get good enough, by combining a natural temperament or attitude with practice and technique, to amaze their friends and sometimes even eke out a living.

Typically the lack of Big Picture understanding, as well as fear, beliefs, ego, and natural access limitations, lead to random and systematic errors. These errors and limitations erode confidence and credibility and prevent individuals from making a big splash among their skeptical reality-mates, though some of their little individual splashes can occasionally be impressive.

You can project your sentience into any of these states and simply look around. Or you can follow a sequence of connected states that produces an effect that is like following a movie frame by frame. Run the frames by fast enough and the action seems realistic – an experience – exactly like being there. Because all possible choices are available, you can theoretically make the story line run any way you want to, but it is much more useful to follow variations of your personal choices and let all the other virtual players make only their most probable moves given the new conditions.

By carefully using your focused intent, you can design and create almost any query-filter you can imagine, apply it to this database, and **experience** the results. The experienced end product is exactly like being there. Imagine a 3D holographic movie where you control the conditions or filter-sets that define the possibilities and probabilities of the action. Lack of specificity adds random or nominal components to the filter definitions intended. If you do not know enough to define and control the process precisely, the results appear to be jumbled and have a mind of their own. In any case, your experience of this data (filtered by your clear or jumbled intent) appears as if you are viewing, and participating in, a reality populated by fully sentient beings with free will. That it is a simulation – a calculation space populated only by probability models of actual beings with free will – would be transparent and thus unnoticeable.

Simulated or emulated digital consciousness does not seem artificial to an individuated digital consciousness with free will. The only difference between you and the emulation of you is that you have the free will necessary to modify the quality of your consciousness. The expectation value driven choices of each modeled player are generally an accurate and realistic representation of that player's quality and intent.

Because of the way errors propagate through a system of unactualized states, the further out (in time) that you go beyond a particular event, the less accurate or meaningful are the results based upon that event. Most errors occur for the following two reasons: Individuals, because of their free will, sometime perform unexpectedly; and, sometimes there are two or more extremely significant (potentially divergent) choices that have nearly equal probabilities of being actualized.

Now that we better understand the attributes of probable reality state vectors and their interactive player probability models, I can be more precise about the process of generating probable realities. Because of natural errors, the value of **M** can only get so large before it no longer makes sense to propagate further generations.

M does not have to remain forever fixed – it is simply easier to initially explain and understand the process that way. Where the probability distributions of discrete events become low and flat (fuzzy results), no further generations (no more child states) are calculated. However, where the distributions remain clear and crisp (high, distinct, peaked, and with individually resolved events), generation after generation is computed until clarity and resolution is lost. As a result, there is a statistical reasonability criterion that determines the number of generations that are propagated forward for any given set of circumstances with **M** being a nominal value.

▶ This short aside will help relax the intensity of the thought (or is that fog?) around your brain: With a little imagination, we could search out a sequence of contiguous states (thread) in the database of OS's unactualized state vectors that might be especially interesting. One interesting pair of threads to compare might be those leading to the Allies winning and also losing WW II – with an alternate (but unactualized) reality movie created by quickly flipping through the state frames of the most likely consequences of different choices. Our history has recorded the terrible price that was paid; now we could also ascertain the value of the benefits gained or lost as a function of time.

Somewhere there is a virtual reality where Saddam Hussein and his army were pursued and destroyed completely during Desert Storm (the US vs. Iraq, Gulf War of 1991). Do you wonder what difference, if any, that might have made? What if John Kennedy, Martin Luther King, Mahatma Gandhi and Jesus had not been killed – where would that leave us now? What if the quarterback hadn't fumbled and you hadn't forgotten your ex-wife's birthday five years in a row? What difference does any particular event make in the long run? I am sure that you can think up many interesting questions relevant to your life.

Your sense of the possibilities is your only limit as to what might be discovered by following a virtual thread along in OS's non-actualized database (past or future) within TBC. You could go there yourself and learn how various historical or personal what-if scenarios would have (most likely) turned out – a great source for writing fiction. In fact, much of our imaginative creativity and inspiration has its source in an intuitive connection to the OS database within TBC. More importantly, it provides a great resource for understanding the impact and importance of your personal choices. As such, it provides an excellent tool for helping you design future experience packets, as well as learn from, and maximize the growth potential of your experience.

A word of caution to those who know how to at least partially open the door of their mind: Do not spend too much energy or time in nonphysical realities or you may neglect or waste the precious time you have in the one reality that is most important to your personal growth – physical reality. Much is perhaps interesting, but only a small subset is pertinent to your personal spiritual growth and therefore important. Do not invest too much time in what is not important. ◀

Back to work. A projection of a fragment of your sentient consciousness into a space-time reality could get spiritually dead-ended in a situation where you **believe** that you do not have significant choices left – you feel that you cannot produce uniquely useful or significant choices during future increments of DELTA-t. Under those circumstances, your inability to find a way out of the perceived dead end will typically cause you to find a way (perhaps a fatal disease or accident) to check out of, or shed, that particular reality. Though most humans do not check out because of being dead-ended, a significant minority do. There are usually many ways out of an imagined dead end, many good choices (other than termination of the experience packet) are typically available, but they remain invisible to a self-referential consciousness limited by belief, fear, and ego.

It should now be clear that because of the choices you make and the objects and beings you interact with, you have considerable influence over the reality in which you develop and evolve your being or consciousness. Interacting significantly with virtual players (mathematical models of yourself and other related beings, objects, and energy) within parallel realities is roughly analogous to playing against the computer in an educational computer game or performing parametric analysis within a simulation. These tools are there for your use, but do not become enamored of them, get unproductively lost in them, or become overly dependent upon them.

Abuse is not widespread because for the most part if you are wise enough to use the available tool sets coherently and powerfully, you are wise enough to use them wisely. The abuse that does occur is usually at low power or of a singular (as opposed to wide spread) nature. The entire structure of NPMR$_N$, including the space-time part, is designed to provide you with the experience and opportunity you need to optimize your learning. The experiences, situations, and opportunities that confront you in

PMR are for the most part the ones your evolving individuated consciousness needs in order to learn what is critical to its continued growth.

The path that you are on is your path of maximum opportunity as designed by you with the help, advice, and cooperation of others. You are involved with your lessons, opportunities, and choices as they define your spiritual evolution and growth within the reality that you and your co-conspirators (others who are significant to your existence or being) are producing.

What can you or others do that is significant enough to effect a change in the quality of your consciousness? Significant, within this context, means potentially capable of path-altering and life-changing effects. If the overall results of your **potentially** significant choice don't actually make a significant difference to you or anyone else (who might be affected by your choice), then that choice contains little power to effect a change in the quality of your consciousness.

When some guy, for example, makes an important choice, perhaps to marry and have children with that lovely woman he has been dating for the past five years, popping the question produces choices for her, her family, her roommate, her landlord, his mother, his other girlfriends, and so on. All affected are in an interactive dance that alters everyone's personal reality as each make their choices. If the same man makes a choice to scratch his head with his right hand instead of his left hand, as is his habit, nothing significant is either affected or effected – no opportunities for growth are likely produced – it is an insignificant act that does not have to be tracked.

▶ Keep in mind that significance in the Big Picture is about changing the quality (entropy) of your consciousness while significance in the little picture is most often related to satisfying the needs, wants, desires, and expectations of your ego. Trivial choices with a low probability of Big Picture significance can be safely ignored. Calculations of the probability of significance do not have to be perfect – if they are consistent and reasonable, a working virtual reality can be functionally defined. Given the interactive complexity and purpose of PMR, consistency and the continual availability of a rich array of significant choices are much more important than accuracy in every minute detail. By ignoring choices that are expected to be trivial, the requirement for computational resources to compute the likely consequences of virtual reality interactions is greatly reduced. Likewise, the computations of consequences do not have to be perfect. Absolute precision of each event and its interactions and eventual outcome (as required by determinism) is incompatible with a finite, statistics based digital virtual reality.

Extreme precision in defining and progressing each event is not important to the purpose of PMR. As long as the psi uncertainty principle constrains the mechanics of reality to present the appearance of an interactive objective causal reality to the individuated units of consciousness evolving within PMR, the functionality, value, and purpose of PMR is adequately maintained. Physicists working from a deterministic model of reality have been tripping over this conceptual error ever since Isaac Newton uncovered a few significant pieces of PMR's space-time rule-set. Their insistence that all phenomena be forced into a deterministic causal model has blinded them to the true nature of the reality they are trying to understand.

Even statistics based quantum mechanics is coerced to exist within a deterministic straight jacket; the statistical description at the root is seen as only a nebulous intermediate step before the final states collapse to some measurable physical reality. The joke is: The statistical description represents the actual reality while the resultant final physical state represents only a virtual shadow of the more fundamental statistical reality. Getting it wrong is normal enough, but believing it to be the exact opposite of how it actually is adds a touch of humor to the sanctimonious recitation of scientific dogma by the high priests of science. Belief traps and narrow paradigms don't make you stupid; they simply limit your capacity and ability to understand. ◀

The "everything significant that can happen does happen" process would seem to be an excellent experimental design for a spiritual $NPMR_N$. It involves everyone in OS. PMR entities are engaged in a physical experience that constitutes a self-designed consciousness quality increasing, entropy reducing, training class called life that takes place within a learning lab called PMR. In the class of life, within the earth frame of reference, what you do (the choices you make) and the shared reality you live in accurately and inexorably reflects the quality of your being. Additionally, it offers you the specific opportunities (potential choices) you need to enhance the growth of your individuated consciousness.

The meaning, purpose, and direction of all individual and collective consciousness (life) within $NPMR_N$ (of which our PMR is a subset) is focused and animated by the evolutionary requirements of the consciousness cycle and motivated by the purpose of the larger consciousness ecosystem. The fundamental driving imperative is: Evolve! Grow! Become more! Seek out profitability! Reduce the entropy of your consciousness, become animated and motivated by love. To accomplish this evolution revolution, at every level of existence, the Fundamental Process promotes profitability while eliminating failure. If a being is highly sentient, successful evolution requires that this being use its energy to decrease the entropy of its individuated consciousness. By doing so, it decreases the entropy of the entire AUM consciousness system as it decreases the entropy of its own over-soul.

Do you now have some faint notion of the immensity of this reality, and how minute, by comparison, OS and our history are? Given that OS and its history represent a miniscule subset of the possible content that is interacting or stored within the Big Fractal Picture, how much more minute, by comparison, is our physical universe, our solar system, earth, humanity, and you? Small, yes! But, we are still significant. Very significant indeed! Notice how small a virus or a bacterium seems to us and how viruses and bacteria are not only significant, but also vital to our physical existence. Imagine how small a hydrogen atom must seem to a virus – are hydrogen atoms significant and critical to our continued existence? Imagine how small a neutrino must seem to an atom – are neutrino's significant? Yes! All are very significant! You have now seen how the Big Picture of your immediate (local) reality works – this is not necessarily the mechanics of the biggest picture, but it is extremely big relative to our typical PMR view all the same. Is your view of our immediate larger reality like the atom's view of a human? Maybe.

If your sense of personal importance or significance is shattered by the sheer size of the bigger picture, you should concentrate on playing your part (your important part) to the best of your ability. You should focus on maximizing every opportunity to grow the quality of your being – the success of which is reflected by the choices you make. Be your best and don't worry too much about the small stuff, or the big stuff. Just be. That's what the neutrinos, atoms and viruses do – and hey, who ever heard of an unhappy neutrino, a neurotic atom, or a depressed virus?

11
■■■

Ramifications
Changing the Future,
Changing the Past, and
the Quantization of Time
■■■

Let us pull together and summarize what we have learned thus far. This short condensation and solidification of the concepts presented in the previous several chapters will get us ready to explore the ramifications of existing and experiencing within a virtual digital reality. This is where the fun starts, but first we need to make sure that we have a firm grip on the basics.

1. Future Probabilities are Non-Binding – Things can Change

We can say that the past, present, and future all occur and exist within TBC simultaneously – if by future we mean the probable un-actualized (potential) realities. The future is not a done deal; it exists only as a complete set of probable futures with varying probability densities (peaks on the surface) forming and changing around possible future events. All these states exist within TBC at the same time. All are fertile and capable of producing new child states given a change in initial conditions. All can be visited and experienced by an appropriately aware consciousness. Consider the many software applications, simulations, and folders sitting in your computer. They are all extant at the same time, all are ready to do whatever they do, some are dynamically executing (running, changing, operating, incrementing local time) while others are idle awaiting input or simply storing results.

Some probable reality surface peaks (within a dynamically executing reality) may be narrow, indicating a more precise probable time of potential actualization, while others are broad, indicating larger uncertainty in the time of potential actualization. These probability densities (peaks) may vary like the topology of any other surface function, in amplitude, width, shape, and area under the curve. As DELTA-t increments and our PMR time moves on, choices (random and sentient) are made and one of the potential future states is actualized into the present. This creates a new set of probabilities and expectations about what might happen next. The entire set of future possibilities is recalculated after each DELTA-t.

Because our future is both dynamic (updated every DELTA-t) and statistical, it exists only as a set of uncertain probable realities; consequently, it has a fundamentally different nature than our past (which is the set of stored reality system state vectors that were actualized by the beings, objects, and energy of OS). Although many future events are accurately predictable (which is the basis for precognition) because of high expectation values, they have not yet been actualized or chosen into the OS present – and things can and do change. This is why Eastern traditions talk only about past lives and not future lives and why karma is attached only to past events and situations, not future ones. We have not yet actualized our future – it could turn out to be any one of a large set of possibilities, some being more likely than others. We turn the probable future into our present by making our collective choices and thus removing all uncertainty.

The probable future is ours to peruse within limits set for our own good. An individual, a group, or an event can have its future probable reality surface calculated – it simply depends on how you want to filter or query the probable future database and whether the circumstances support your being granted access to the data. Access must be both earned by you and granted by the system administrator.

Having someone else retrieve the data for you will not get you around the access problem. Access is granted by the system administrator based on the probable use of the data, not on who retrieves it. There is no way to cheat, trick, or force the system into providing information that will not produce a positive spiritual benefit for all who might be affected by it.

One can modify the probable future surface with focused intent, thereby raising or lowering the expectation value of a future possibility. With a properly focused mind, new peaks can sometimes appear and others of long standing may slowly disappear from the probable reality surface representing a given entity. This is generally how the mind utilizes nonphysical mental energy to manipulate future events within PMR without violating the psi uncertainty principle. The psi uncertainty principle tells us that fuzzy short peaks are easier to modify than tall sharp ones and that events become increasingly more and more difficult to manipulate the closer they get to the present.

▶ I said "slowly disappear" in the previous paragraph out of practical considerations not because slowness is theoretically necessary. The organizational energy that created that peak in the first place must be dissipated in order to remove or reduce that events expectation value. If an event's expectation (future probability of being actualized) still has energy being poured into it, that energy must be dissipated as well if its associated peak is to be eliminated. Your mind, depending on your quality, interest, and instantaneous access privileges, can only apply so much power (do so much work per unit time) to reorganize the digital energy that represents the expectation you are trying to change. Your ability to manipulate bits is limited and must compete with the ability of others to intentionally or unintentionally manipulate those same bits.

In Chapter 13, Book 2, we used the term "force of being" and said:

Constraints come in many forms. For example, if someone who has the ability to manipulate nonphysical energy is asked to remove (dissipate or dematerialize) a tumor (noticeable lump) from someone's PMR body, the energy required is dependent upon, among other things, the degree to which this tumor is connected to PMR reality – its force of being in PMR. Quantitatively [force of being is associated with] the expectation value of the future event. If the body's owner and a few others are mildly distressed about the **possibility** *of a malignant tumor, the removal energy may be relatively low (easy to accomplish). In this situation, much uncertainty exists within PMR – but not necessarily for the one viewing and manipulating the body's nonphysical energy from within NPMR – to that person, both the physical and nonphysical properties of the lump may be clear.*

If, on the other hand, four doctors and half the residents at the local hospital have looked at the CAT scan or felt the lump and are relatively certain the tumor is malignant, the removal energy is somewhat higher. When all of the above get the biopsy report confirming a fast growing, incurable, always-deadly malignancy, the required energy increases. The more firmly the malignant tumor's existence and likely outcome (degree of causal certainty) is held and shared in the minds and expectations of credible sentient beings, the taller and denser its probability function becomes. The uncertainty of the outcome dissipates and the probable event of dying in PMR from this cancer becomes much more difficult to change by manipulating energy in NPMRN. Fortunately, the intent and attitude (mental focus) of the body's owner has the greatest potential impact. Unfortunately, this attitude is often driven by its fear and the opinions and fears of others.

Now, by definition, it takes a miracle, where before no miracle was required. The confident knowledge of the doctors, which is based on test results and historical precedent (mortality statistics), actually affects (decreases) the probability of actualization of other alternative possibilities *such as the cancer spontaneously going into remission, or the tumor turns out to be benign. As in quantum mechanics, performing the measurement forces the result to pick a state compatible with PMR causality (compatible with the PMR space-time rule-set). Typically, the most likely state at the time of the measurement is picked unless there are several states of equal probability, then one outcome is picked randomly from among the set of outcomes (future states) that are all most likely. The individual with the tumor, along with his or her friends and loved ones, can inadvertently help drive the final outcome to an unhappy ending by causing the probability of a fatal outcome to grow, and the probability of a non-fatal outcome to shrink. Beware: you can be easily drawn into a fatal dance of expectation with those connected to you, or to your condition. The best time for intervention, whether from PMR or NPMR, is long before "fatal" becomes a near inevitability.*

Now you can understand what was being said from a much broader perspective. The terms "density" and "force of being" refer to the cumulative amount of digital energy of organization invested in a given expectation or peak on the future probable reality surface. The more digital energy that is collectively and individually invested in a given outcome, the more resistant its expectation value (likelihood of future actualization) is to change.

Digital energy can accumulate just as physical energy can (charge in a battery or water being pumped into a tall tank). Just because you know how to reorganize bits and manipulate digital energy within the lager consciousness ecosystem, doesn't mean you can do whatever you want. Even if you obtain the necessary access and permission (which are not always easy to get and are granted on a case by case basis), you still have a limited ability to change events that exhibit a strong force of being. Yours is not the only intent and organizing force active within OS. There are limits to what you can do in NPMR, just like there are limits to what you can do in PMR – and for much the same reasons.

All realties, all virtual existences, operate according to their own causality (rule-sets) and you must live and operate interactively within those rules. Forget about your ego-dream of becoming superman or a miracle worker – those represent an exceptionally poor choice of goals. Existence is not about having it your way or impressing your friends. Nor is it about helping your fellow humans to be healthier, happier, and more comfortable. Given the right intent, those may be very worthwhile activities that help you focus and improve your learning within PMR, however, your existence is about **you** individually increasing the quality of **your** consciousness and, where possible, facilitating others to do the same. Spiritual growth is a personal accomplishment that must be achieved individually by each unit of individuated consciousness whether that unit is you, your puppy dog, or the Big Cheese. Helping others is necessarily on the path to that accomplishment but it is a byproduct, not the final goal or endpoint. ◀

State vectors are not closed systems; outside energy, beings and objects can interact at any time. TBC simply keeps up with all the changes and their effects. Our reality is dynamic, interactive and uncertain because that is the nature of individuated consciousness.

There is no conflict between free will, and predestination or precognition. Visions of the future are simply visions of probable realities. The past (all stored reality system state vectors, whether we have actualized them or not) is alive, vibrant, available, open to us (for inspection or what-if analysis) through $NPMR_N$, and fully capable of calculating new realities based upon new initial conditions. Future probable reality surfaces are generated (for each state of OS, each DELTA-t) by looking at only the most probable states that exist downstream among our unactualized future possibilities.

State vectors can be perceived either singly or strung sequentially together as frames of a movie. You can experience probable future states (as a nonphysical interacting observer) by focusing your intent while sentient in $NPMR_N$ (like experiencing a movie from a god's eye view). The probability, likelihood, or expectation value of each and every potential future state is known, but it may or may not be available to you (along with other details of the future).

You may or may not be blocked from knowing the probable future by information filters that reflect a concern with the impact that this knowledge might have on the evolving quality of your consciousness – just as an adult would prevent children from playing with fire, or accessing inappropriate material on TV, or on the World Wide Web (WWW). It is **your** quality, **your** degree of consciousness development (lack of entropy), which determines what you can and cannot clearly experience – regardless of who is receiving the data. If future probabilities are shut off from your knowing, the problem may be one of simple ignorance – you simply may not know how to access the information. Or perhaps a limit has been placed on your access to knowledge by wiser entities who are aware of existing intrinsic personal limitations, and who are looking out for your best interests. For example, you may cause more harm than good to the process of developing the quality of your consciousness if the motivation for gaining the information is in the service of your ego, for personal material gain, or likely to feed or encourage other high entropy intents.

2. Changing the Past

Our past (the history of OS) can be thought of as a series, or thread of actualized states. Because TBC stores **all** results at the end of each

DELTA-t interval, our past (as well as other non-actualized past possibilities) continue to exist and are accessible through $NPMR_N$. You may decide to modify the actualized past by projecting a fragment of your consciousness into a reality described by a time now past but still defined in TBC with its associated DELTA-t. (You may make the trip by decrementing DELTA-t along our history thread to that past point in time or simply specify the time, place, and reality frame). At this point, you may use your focused free will intent to follow the thread of a specifically different set of choices and a specifically different set of conditions than those that were actualized. The resultant possible but unactualized past that you create is experienced as an entirely unique and realistic set of sequential happenings with which you may actively interact. However, because you can process only so much data per unit time, you will be aware only of those interactions that you specify as being of interest to you.

Relative to the participating observer, it **appears** as if the initial conditions of the beginning state vector have been changed to reflect the observer's new choices and conditions, and that all the various players (represented by predictive mathematical models) interact with those changed initial conditions by modifying their choices, intents, and actions. The observer sees a new reality, based on the new initial conditions that he or she brought to the starting point, branch from the original. The process repeats and continues as long as the observer maintains his focus and is interested in seeing what happens next. Interacting or experiencing within this new series of events appears to be identical to interacting or experiencing within the present OS reality.

That the other players are mathematical models that do not exercise free will is entirely transparent and undetectable because the database contains **all** significant possibilities ordered by their expectation values. It simply appears to the participating observer driving this re-write of history that a new reality has branched from the historical beginning point (state vector) where he first changed the initial conditions based on a modified free will input to that system. Another way of looking at this is that the observer is implementing a specific series of dynamic queries of the TBC database by his intent.

The old thread (our history) is not changed or affected in any way. It continues to increment (move forward in time), unperturbed by the apparent new branch diverging from that old (past) DELTA-t. From the perspective of TBC, no new reality is created – previously stored data from the everything-that-could-happen-does-happen database is merely being accessed and ordered differently. As you modify the input data (choices) within any given state vector new probability configurations and expectation values (for yourself or for others) are automatically computed. No new files or reality state vectors are created or stored; you are simply exploring the possibilities within a virtual simulation. This virtual simulation allows one to explore probable event-chains or causal threads within a higher order virtual simulation. Having a simple virtual simulator within a more complex larger virtual simulation might seem a tad confusing, but that is simply the nature of digital reality. Employing simulations within simulations within simulations is similar to utilizing nested subroutines or sub-simulations – a common programming practice within PMR and NPMR.

The OS database of unactualized possibilities within TBC may be viewed, queried, explored, experienced, or lived in unique new ways based upon the intent of the participating observer. While exploring this database, what you do **outside** your reality **may** create the experience of new realities, but it imposes no new data on TBC, nor does it affect your home reality (OS) except in as much as it changes the quality of your consciousness (providing the experience precipitated learning and growth).

Only what you do with your free will choices **inside** your larger reality from either PMR or NPMR can change that reality directly (for the one who is making the changes as well as for others). This is true of individual interaction within any past or probable future set of states within TBC's calculation-space. One might say that the participating observer executing the what-if analysis is working only with a volatile scratch copy of the original state file so that the changes he makes provides the full experience of an operational reality but leaves no permanent record. From another equivalent viewpoint, it is clear that running a dynamic query filter does not alter the original data set. Though your what-if analysis leaves no permanent trace, a generated experience (unique tour through the data) can be reconstituted from the original data anytime.

Our PMR past (as well as unactualized past possibilities) is always alive and well in TBC. The **experiencing** of new pasts, represented by either the reality branching or database querying viewpoints previously described, are always available and accessible via the RWW. Whether you see this process as a database query or the branching of a new reality is relative to your perspective. Both views are identical – it is only a matter of your frame of reference. Thus in summary, you may create and experience a new reality that branches from some past or probable future state vector by introducing new initial conditions into the beginning state, or equivalently, you may trace a unique path through TBC's database of unactualized past or future possibilities.

Your present fragment in this present reality (what and where you think you are now) is not necessarily the main one. Mostly there is no main one – all your various projections into various present states within various reality systems containing beings with free will are merely different. All these divergent realities (sometimes called parallel realities because they are initially similar to each other or may share a common state) exist simultaneously in $NPMR_N$ as books all exist simultaneously in the library or files and folders all exist simultaneously in the computer. Imagine every OS state vector since the beginning of space-time time, as well as all those projected $\mathbf{M} \cdot (DELTA\text{-}t)$ into the future, existing within a huge on-line database in TBC. The past, present and probable future of OS all exist simultaneously within one database – a database that is accessible by the queries you design and execute with your intent.

The present is unique because it contains the actual ongoing virtual reality game or happening in which the players exercise free will. It constitutes the learning lab and generates the direct experience that provides custom designed original opportunity to learn and to grow the quality of your consciousness. Everything else is the result of calculating and storing the possibilities – data manipulation built upon the analysis of previous free will choices. Though these manipulations produce some fine experiential educational tools, life's game of consciousness evolution is played, for the most part, in the present moment.

New potential realities are constantly being generated from present choices. Likewise, modified histories are available for you to experience as your intent follows any number of possible threads winding their way through TBC's state vector database. As free will choices are made, particular possibilities are actualized into the present. The present becomes the past when the next DELTA-t time increment is initiated. This actualized history is generated by the beings, objects, and energy that interactively coexist in a particular present reality state at a given time increment DELTA-t. Every actualized and unactualized reality state vector, representing all variables, possibilities, and probabilities for each DELTA-t, is saved in the state vector database, so that **all** possible realities, beginning with the first DELTA-t, simultaneously coexist within TBC. These saved state vectors are open to the possibility of a change of variables or initial conditions so that additional learning can be squeezed from a what-if analysis that illuminates the long and short term impacts of a given choice or series of choices.

If AUM thought that a particular state vector was particularly interesting or held particular promise, he could use it as a pattern to generate another (or many) evolutionary experimental branch populated with entities with free wills. Because we and all else (including AUM) are digital, it could simply start with a copy of the original (such as OS) and then make modifications as required before setting it off to evolve on its own. Thus, there is another level of parallel realities that evolve on their own, are populated by entities with free will, and are not merely uniquely filtered output reports of existing data. Some of the various independent PMRs share common states on their history threads (one is a branch of the other).

You (your present consciousness awareness) can visit any state of any reality system anytime as an observer by focusing your intent while sentient in $NPMR_N$. If you significantly interact with any of these states while in $NPMR_N$ or become experientially aware in them and have a significant potential to direct the action with your free will intent, you will have an opportunity to learn and grow from the experience.

The generation of a unique reality branch does not modify or change other previously existing reality states or sequence of states. What was, and what is, continues undisturbed on its merry way, unaffected by either the creation of what-if branches within the calculation-space of TBC, or the creation of new niches within the greater consciousness ecosystem fractal.

A common sci-fi plot element requires changes in the present and future to follow instantaneously from inadvertent or purposeful changes to the past (usually made by a nefarious or bungling time traveler). The idea that any change affects everything downstream is based on the erroneous assumption of a continuous reality instead of a digital one and a fundamental misunderstanding of the functional relationships that interconnect the past, present, and future. Fiddling with OS's unactualized or actualized past has no affect on the existing OS data within TBC and no affect on the present choices being made. The one extremely important effect it does have is to provide learning opportunities to individuated units of aware consciousness that result in a decrease of the unit's entropy. Simply running a query that results in a custom build-as-you-go interactive holographic movie output report does not change the data in the database – but it may change you. And you may change future intents and choices that will define future states.

3. The Significance of Quantized Time and the Concept of an Even Bigger Computer (EBC)

Let us re-examine quantized time and TBC from the bigger picture perspective of multiple PMRs each within their own OS and progressing along by incrementing their own time increments. I will let the subscript k differentiate and enumerate these various other OS-PMR-DELTA-t type systems. Time will accumulate in these systems by adding up all the DELTA-t time quanta that have been sequentially incremented within that system.

Using this notation, our OS is only one of multiple OS_k simulations in TBC, each having its own PMR_k. The total elapsed time from the beginning of time (the first DELTA-t_k in each PMR_k) is T_k. Here, $T_k = K_k$ (DELTA-t_k) where K_k is an integer, specific to each PMR_k. DELTA-t_k is defined as the time quanta of OS_k, and is the smallest discrete time increment within PMR_k. Time in any PMR_k seems continuous because DELTA-t_k is so small. Each virtual physical reality represented by a PMR_k runs on its own local time defined by incrementing its own DELTA-t_k. As far as I can tell, all the DELTA-t_k are about the same size. However, different PMR_k may have different values of K_k, and therefore different values of T_k. Among the PMR_k within their respective OS_k, there are often shared beginnings with major decision points creating branches where OS_k and OS_{k+1} go off their own way – an attribute that only a digital reality can easily manage.

It is quantized time and the storage medium in TBC that allows history to remain alive and vital as a seed for additional virtual realities and as an educational tool set.

It is quantized time and digital processing that allows independent branching of realities so that a change to a past state does not cause subsequent, automatic, and instantaneous change to occur in the future belonging to that past.

It is quantized time that allows discrete and independent reality system state vectors, each with a probable future.

Quantized time allows the probable future to be progressed and tailored efficiently to each discrete state vector.

Quantized time gives TBC control and flexibility because it can stop incrementing (pause) T_k after any particular DELTA-t_k increment for as long as it likes (time literally stands still) and then start it back up again without noticeable effects. AUM-EBC-TBC, due to the characteristics and properties of digital simulation, can at any time take (copy) any reality state vector, modify its initial conditions and let it be the seed for a new virtual reality experience simulator learning lab. That is analogous to taking the best or most interesting bacteria found growing in all the petri dishes and using them as the basis for a new set of experiments.

Quantization and the digital nature of TBC also allow TBC (to the extent that TBC is fast enough) to speed up or slow down any specific reality PMR_k by incrementing the DELTA-t_k as fast as it wants (not to exceed as fast as it can) relative to $NPMR_N$ real-time by adjusting the size of (DELTA-t_k) or modifying the time base defining the fundamental **simulation** time quanta delta-t_k.

Because of the properties of digital simulation, AUM and TBC could rewind our reality movie or do any number of tricks (similar to the magical things we do by manipulating digital audio and video in our computers). Fortunately for us, tricks for the sake of tricks eventually become boring and disturb serious science projects. This type of meddling in ongoing consciousness systems is not often done. AUM is not merely a big kid playing computer games. Sure, AUM might create a reality-dimension or two for amusement or gaming, but it has nothing to do with our local reality (OS) – unless of course, we **are** the fun one. I am having fun, aren't you?

Because of quantized or incremented time, TBC can run our play, our reality movie, in fast forward or reverse as well as in slow motion or pause it (relative to time in $NPMR_N$). Our sense of time, our PMR time, is thus an **artificial construct** relative to time as it exists in $NPMR_N$. Likewise, $NPMR_N$ time is an artificial construct relative to time as it exists in NPMR. AUM is the dude with the smallest time quanta – that fact puts it in charge – as the originator of the fundamental beat that everyone else must dance to. Think of PMR as a subroutine in a larger simulation that is incremented by DELTA-t because the objects, energy, and beings it models only change infinitesimally relative to one DELTA-t.

Quantized time allows AUM, or whatever part of AUM is designing the software for EBC, to control the experiments or the consciousness cycle for optimal results. The Space-Time N-Division Management Team can collect and further manipulate the data it generates. It can easily terminate unproductive scenarios and rerun particularly interesting ones with or without new input data or new random number seeds. Because consciousness and thus reality is digital, N-Division's Management Team can easily update hardware or software, and modify experimental design on the fly without disturbing the experiments. AUM's experiments are flexible and optimized to capture all possible outcomes – they create their own complete set of result statistics about evolving consciousness. All such digital machinations are completely transparent to the players – they, for the most part, remain completely clueless within a reality that, by design, always appears physical and continuous.

Quantized time and digital processing allows for the simultaneous discrete existence of a variable number of multiple projections of you. It allows TBC and other sentient beings that are aware in $NPMR_N$ to run what-if analysis by providing a dynamic representation (mathematical model) of all the players and all the possible significant conditions.

The time in $NPMR_N$ appears to be fundamental and continuous to its residents. Nevertheless, it is merely a higher level loop in the simulated time construct that is defined or manufactured within EBC and TBC. Although we know that the passage of time in $NPMR_N$ is created by a series of even smaller quantized time increments, you would not be able to experientially notice or measure that small a time increment from within $NPMR_N$ because of your local perspective in that reality. Similarly, you cannot be aware of $NPMR_N$ from the limited local perspective of PMR. To become aware within the reality that is **parenting** $NPMR_N$, you must gain the perspective of the next higher level in the reality onion. You have the proper vantage point to analyze the dynamics, content and structure of a reality only from the perspective of the next level of generality.

From an $NPMR_N$ perspective, NPMR and beyond represents a reality that appears mystical and lies beyond the logical causality of the residents of $NPMR_N$. A detailed exploration of the mechanics of NPMR would require a sentient perspective from the next higher level of organization **beyond** the various $NPMR_n$. All the various $NPMR_n$ seem to run on independent, though similarly derived, time bases.

From my experience, I can clearly **infer** a larger system (run within the EBC – Even Bigger Computer) representing another higher level of organization within AUM wherein TBC is either emulated within an outer loop or simply a subset of the EBC. This larger system is dynamically driven by a time quantum that is much smaller than the one that animates OS.

I have not yet **directly** experienced such a reality as a well-defined understandable place with well-defined rules. I do not yet know how to interpret those experience data within my limited NPMR and $NPMR_n$ level of awareness. When dealing with phenomena that relate to reality systems beyond $NPMR_n$, I am like a PMR scientist working with atoms and electrons that he or she can infer, but cannot directly experience. Such a scientist can experience only the effects of atoms and electrons, but not the atoms and electrons themselves.

That gives me something to work on in my spare time. I have been exploring NPMR, $NPMR_N$, OS, and PMR for only thirty years – there is much that I have not yet seen and experienced. Perhaps the $NPMR_n$ represent the outermost layer of our **practical** (operational) reality onion, leaving NPMR as a simple $NPMR_n$ container or media – and only AUM beyond that. One must eventually run into the outer edges of the greater consciousness ecosystem, the boundary of the AUM-reality itself.

That AUM is perhaps a single cell populating the lower intestine of an AUMosaurus is probably far beyond the reach of AUM's awareness. You and I should not feel too bad if we do not get that far.

12

■ ■ ■

Ramifications
Communications, Time Travel,
and Teleportation

■ ■ ■

Communications

Apparent PMR distances or spatial separation does not affect signal quality on the RWW net within $NPMR_N$. For example, an earthbound individual would experience no noticeable time lag between questions and answers if he were telepathically carrying on a conversation with someone located near Alpha Centauri (a star 4.4 light-years away from the earth). Transmission time and variations in signal-to-noise ratio are likewise not noticeably affected by a perceived separation between the sender and the receiver even if each is in different PMRs or in different $NPMR_n$ – much as a web page (as seen by my browser) hosted on a server in Australia is as clearly and quickly represented on my monitor as a web page hosted on a server in the next room. It would appear to take no longer to access one grouping of data (dimension) within TBC as any other – distance is only virtual and has no meaning outside of the virtual PMR_k.

Time Travel and Teleportation

Energy (the ability to rearrange bits and affect organization, and thus content, within a system) from $NPMR_N$ can be directed to any PMR_k at any point on its thread of actualized history, including our PMR as a particular instance of PMR_k. Because energy can propagate between any PMR_k and any $NPMR_n$, (as well as between everything else that is on the NPMR RWW net), there seems to be no a priori reason why **what we perceive and experience** as physical matter could not be transported either directly, or by using NPMR$_N$ as an intermediate hub or router, between realities within NPMR$_N$. The same goes for conscious embodied beings.

In fact, because physical reality is only a virtual reality (a rule-set that defines the experience of individuated consciousness within the space-time subset of AUM), jumping or teleporting from one experience-set to another one in a different time and place would not seem impossible. Dimension hopping between realities is not so difficult. Because all is consciousness, it would seem that teleporting through what appears to you as time or space would merely be a matter of getting around within TBC.

How could an AI Guy in a WWII war game simulation, get into the WWI or Viet Nam war game simulation running in the same computer? He would need to know, understand, and be able to operate within the larger computer reality. He would need to be able to copy his algorithms, memory and data (himself) into the other simulation and insert himself properly into the appropriate time loop drivers. He would need to understand the content and mechanics of the new simulation enough to modify the code of the new simulation host to integrate himself (share data) into that simulation in a useful way.

Do you see the levels above his local reality in which he would have to operate in order to teleport into a totally different simulation? But what if he wanted only to teleport around within his own simulation – perhaps be two places at the same time? That's much easier but he still needs to be an exceptionally aware and savvy AI Guy in order to modify the data that drives his simulation and to avoid violating the psi uncertainty principle. The same applies to us.

Teleporting a virtual body, which **appears** to be physical, between different local realities is analogous to switching between two virtual reality games – say going from Jungle Safari to Alpine Adventure – entirely possible, but you need to be good at parallel processing and interacting with (programming) the computer. Teleportation is only a matter of switching your consciousness to a different energy packet exchange interface (see Chapter 32, Book 2) after establishing the appropriate data links so that all interactions with other players are properly taken into account. That may seem challenging but is not as difficult as it sounds. The user interface between an individuated consciousness aware in NPMR$_N$ and TBC simplifies most of the required actions.

Fortunately, there is little advantage, need, or incentive for you to take your PMR body along as you explore the best sites on the RWW. Keep in mind that what is physical is relative to the observer. We appear to be nonphysical to other PMRs as they appear to be nonphysical to us. Thus, the idea of dragging a **physical** body to other reality frames makes no sense. There is no physical body, except in your mind. Teleporting a **physical** body has meaning only within your own local reality where you must figure out a way around the psi uncertainty principle. It is much easier and more practical to manifest an **additional** body appropriate to the place visited. Possessing multiple bodies in multiple realities is not a problem.

Why bother teleporting? There is little advantage and no point to dragging a unique body around with you wherever you go. Being either apparently physical or nonphysical in several reality dimensions at one time is not difficult if you can parallel process sufficiently well. Having one unique identical body at two places at the same time within the same reality stresses the psi uncertainty requirements more than having two physically different bodies at two locations at the same time. Having one physical body and one or more nonphysical bodies in the same physical reality at the same time does not stress the psi uncertainty principle.

Actually, I cannot imagine a situation where anyone's spiritual growth would be enhanced by teleporting a physical body around within a single physical reality. It is simply not important, and not worth much effort. On the other hand, though it is entirely irrelevant in the Big Picture, it certainly would be lots of fun – imagine all the great gags you could pull. Also, it would be convenient (like being rich) as well as save transportation costs and travel time. If great gags and convenience are your goals, get working on it. Beam me up, Scottie.

Teleporting your awareness (nonphysical body) is less complicated because the objective physical experience connection to the space-time rule-set (your physical body) is left behind undisturbed. Traveling with only the consciousness is simpler than manifesting an additional body because local psi uncertainty principles are more easily satisfied. The mind is free to go, be aware, and experience anything anywhere on the Big Picture reality net (with a few access restrictions). Many PMR residents do not comprehend this; consequently, they never go anywhere – they simply stay at home and baby-sit their bodies. They have no idea there is a wholly new and magnificent reality out there to explore – or how important it is to the success of their mission – or for that matter, that there even is a purpose or mission to their life. They have their you-know-what stuck in a belief trap. Contrary to popular opinion, ignorance is not bliss, it is just ignorance.

Unique addresses exist for any 3D space-time point or being in any PMR (the same goes for points and beings outside space-time). Conscious beings, embodied or not, can use their minds as a vehicle to directly, or by using NPMR$_N$ as an intermediate hub or router, transport their awareness between any two points within our PMR (our universe) or within the larger reality. Think of it as hopping between different clumps of memory cells or locations in TBC. Using local coordinates that uniquely define a particular state vector, your consciousness awareness can end up anywhere you want it to in the reality of your choice.

Thus for example, you can make a custom designed worm hole from a point in your present space-time-reality to a point on our shared history thread, or to any other space-time-reality point in any other reality (our PMR or not, our history thread or not). This process is successfully and commonly used by beings (embodied in PMR or not) that are sentient in NPMR$_N$. Navigation of your awareness is consciously directed by focused intent over a low noise background and is limited by the extent of your knowledge and your experience. As long as there is a unique destination URL or address (and you know what it is – or know someone who knows), you can navigate to any dimension, reality, place (local coordinates), person (unique consciousness ID), or thing.

The address reads as any other, from the more general to the more specific. Say you want to check out the healing process of a stomach ulcer that is bothering a good friend of yours who lives in some other PMR, the address might be as simple as: reality, individual, stomach, ulcerated cells – as long as the individual was unique within that reality. You mail your energy or consciousness by intent (see Topics 5 through 9 in Chapter 4 of this book). Essentially this is how remote viewers (RV) and out-of-body experiencers (OOBE), as well as other mind travelers, get to and from wherever they go, whether they express it like this or not.

Clear and complete intent is critical. Knowing you need a city and street but being unaware that a state and house number are also required to find a particular resident creates a large **set** of possible solutions because some cities in different states may have the same name and many cities have the same street names. If intent is not clear and informed about how to specify the uniqueness of an address (at all levels of the address), those parts of the address that are not sufficiently specific are often filled in with a random selection from, or a smear across, (depending on the circumstances) the possible solution set. Unfortunately, the explorer often never knows that randomness or inaccuracy has crept into his vision. If the intent is foggy or imprecise, the results might be foggy (smeared across the possibilities) or they might be clear but inaccurate (random selection).

Given the numbers of multiple realities and given that similar reality branches could be almost identical in certain areas (unrelated to the uniqueness that created the branch in the first place), it is easy to understand that getting the right address (knowing what you are doing) becomes more and more difficult the farther you stray from home (going beyond your comfortable understanding). This is, and has always been, a common problem of all explorers – from Christopher Columbus to Lewis and Clark to Captain Kirk. The solution? Carefully and continually turn very small parts of what is unknown into what is known. It is a slow, time consuming process, and in NPMR, must be accomplished by each explorer by and for himself.

No one can give you a detailed map of the territory, but they can give you specific addresses. Successful travelers (those who have controlled out-of-body-experiences or who successfully practice remote-viewing) understand the importance of a clear address, the need to suspend the noisy ego, and the necessity for many hours of developmental experience to guide the way.

Once you have projected your awareness from NPMR to any reality-system state vector (past or probable-future, actualized or non-actualized, OS or otherwise), you can easily specify your intent and let DELTA-t run forward or backward from that point of entry to make a realistic movie from the sequential frames. However, you must be careful at branch points to not get sidetracked into a reality other than the one intended. As you might imagine, it is easy to get lost and turned around – your intent must be unique (which is sometimes difficult because often you are not aware of all the variables), steady, clear, and complete. Anything else may well invoke that old computer-programming truism: Garbage in, garbage out. Awareness of the potential difficulties and plenty of carefully evaluated experience are the only remedies.

Flying Faster than a Speeding Photon, and the Art of Generating Multiple Bodies That Simultaneously Belong to Your Present Personal Awareness.

Warp speed is perhaps not important if you can simply materialize yourself and your spaceship from any space-time-reality to any other space-time-reality. It would be like sending a matter-gram of yourself over the reality net by plugging your conscious awareness into some other reality's experience simulator. If you choose the same PMR reality, you will merely teleport around within the same universe – again, uncertainty (as required by the psi-uncertainty principle) must obscure problematical rule-set viola-tions at both ends and within all PMRs. When you realize your body and your spaceship are only rule-set based experiential delusions of mass by a hallucinating nonphysical consciousness, the concept of warp speeds, the necessity for spaceships, and teleporting take on new meaning.

Splitting, duplicating, or fragmenting is a natural thing for your con-sciousness to accomplish. There is no rule or law that demands only one **apparently physical** body at one time at one location in one space-time-reality. As long as the rules of interaction are obeyed and the psi uncer-tainty principle (described in Chapters 13 and 14 of Book 2) is met, AUM and the Big Cheese are happy campers.

The idea that you must take the body-energy with you by dematerializ-ing or disengaging from your shared experience here (from the viewpoint of others here) and then re-materializing or engaging a shared physical experience somewhere else is based on a misunderstanding of the nature of reality. For some reason, it seems intuitive to citizens of PMR that a body must first disappear (dematerialize) from where it is before it can reappear (materialize) somewhere else. Because your body is only a vir-tual one to begin with, all this materializing and dematerializing is silly. It is much simpler and more reasonable to create an appropriate form (body) in whatever reality you happen to be in. Fortunately, it does not take much energy to materialize an additional virtual physical body in most virtual simulations within $NPMR_N$. Actually, going bodiless is diffi-cult to do. It would appear that some sort of body that defines the bound-ary of your individuation is automatically attached to your being whether you intend it to be there or not.

In the non-space-time portions of $NPMR_N$ (outside those reality dimen-sions that operate under a space-time rule-set), everything travels faster than warp speeds; accordingly, travel time always **appears** to be instanta-neous and never becomes an issue.

There are rules that dictate how, and to what extent, you can interact in other reality systems – one must observe all local laws including local rule-sets and psi uncertainty.

Dematerializing, materializing, and going faster than light-speed are merely local PMR issues that make little sense in the Big Picture and are not important to your personal growth.

Leaving the PMR Body Behind

We may, in the end, be like old-dog executives who get their secre-taries to make a hard copy of their e-mail before they will read them. In the bigger picture, we resemble the people who do not like teleconferencing because they can't shake hands and do not like telecommuting because they cannot continually watch or monitor their people at work. It may be that we are so used to hauling our bodies around with us that we simply cannot imagine going anywhere without them. Unfortunately, what we cannot imagine becomes impossible to accomplish.

Perhaps in the future, dragging one's body about won't seem necessary or desirable – especially if everything but the virtual body you experience within PMR can easily make the trip. Travel within NPMR is governed entirely by intent. Nonphysical travel within PMR (with all the attendant physical sensations of being there included) has the potential to become more and more like using the telephone, telecommuting, teleconferencing, and communicating via e-mail and the WWW – all concepts of disembodied communications that we are slowly getting used to, and finding extraordinarily efficient.

13

■■■

Ramifications
The Fractal-Like Patterns of Reality
The Seed of the Universe
in the eye of the Gnat

■■■

Interestingly, the basic mechanism that I have described as the genera-
tor of Big Picture reality seems to repeat itself at all levels throughout
the entirety of our reality. Everywhere we look we see the same simple
pattern repeated. From multiple branched diverse actualized and unactualized history traces, to our PMR universe, to the earth's multitude of
diverse species. From our souls, to our cells, to our technology, cities,
and businesses, we see the same Fundamental Process. The Fundamental
Process of evolution is applied repeatedly in the same way that a fractal
generates a higher order representation, a picture or design, by repeti-
tiously applying a pattern at differing scales through a simple relational
mechanism applied recursively. The basic pattern in reality dynamics is
not geometric, but rather one of process, of becoming, of actualization
and evolvement.

The Fundamental Process is as follows: It starts from any point (any
level) of existence or being, spreads out its potentiality into (explores) all
the available possibilities open to its existence, eventually populating only
the states that can maintain significant profitability while letting the others go. The successful states are progressed to their logical conclusions by
iterating the Fundamental Process. Additionally, new or intermediate
states can generate new states. States that no longer hold potential for
profitable growth either disappear or are recombined with others with
which they are redundant. Potential is maintained, in the event new initial or environmental conditions appear.

We saw in the two previous books how this simple process applied to the potential of consciousness generates synergy that develops into low-entropy high-quality consciousness, individuated consciousness, NPMR, time, space-time, OS, PMR, and the entire Big Picture of our reality. In this section we found that the same process enables state vectors, probable future reality surfaces, and everything significant that can happen to happen. Additionally, we have seen how this same process generated our universe, among others, through the Big Digital Bang. Consequently, it should not be surprising that every level of existence, including physical matter and our carbon based biology, follows a similar evolutionary prescription.

Consciousness, the space-time rule-set, and the Fundamental Process together set the boundaries and define the content and dynamics of our local reality. The natural uncertainty expressed by quantum mechanics, psi uncertainty, interactive personal relationship dynamics, as well as the randomness found in nature serve to further stir the pot of possible choices and possible outcomes.

The Fundamental Process of evolution constitutes a reality-generating pattern of applied process. You can notice it everywhere you look. It should be obvious that Darwinian Mechanics followed this same process to successfully populate the earth with diverse life forms – each with uniquely specialized features (such as the human's brain, the frog's tongue, and the multi-faceted eyes of flying insects).

In a more mundane sense, this is also how we humans pursue our daily lives – projecting and calculating potential value into all our known options, choosing the best states or outcomes, and then progressing those forward by our actions and choices. Technologies, businesses, cities, political or financial empires, complex computer software, capitalist markets, corruption, and crab grass, as well as consciousness and sentient beings, all grow, expand, and evolve into the available possibilities by an identical process.

The cells (biology), molecules (chemistry) and atoms (physics) in our bodies (or anywhere else), execute their own version of that same basic process within their given potential or possible states. From the individual particles of high-energy physics, to all PMR and $NPMR_N$ within TBC, we see this simple pattern repeated. Could the Fundamental Process be the mother of all fractals? It is an interesting thought. If true, perhaps we can find the father of all fractals as well.

To be sure, the Fundamental Process does not generate a **geometric fractal**; instead, it produces a **process fractal**. You may need to generalize your concept of fractals, but the similarity to fractal dynamics and structure is obvious. When we look at our reality, we see the results of the evolutionary process repeated at various scales and levels generating intricate convoluted patterns. We see the digital (virtual) energy of synergistic organization creating a complex ecosystem that employs the Fundamental Process to recursively iterate layer after layer of interactive process. Each layer becomes the foundation for the next.

Together, consciousness and the Fundamental Process evolve an ever growing, monstrously complex reality system – a system where every part or entity at every level of existence explores its full potential while populating only those states determined **by itself** (often using criteria germane to the next higher level) to be significant and useful **to itself** (often for a higher level purpose or activity). Solar systems, galaxies, human bodies, insects, and consciousness all evolve through the same pattern (as does everything, including AUM). Why is that simple consistency not surprising?

Beauty and power expressed within elegant simplicity! Does that not appear to you to be a common blueprint or theme from Mother Nature? Absolutely, Occam's razor is based on the truth of it, and most mathematics and natural laws clearly exhibit those characteristics. Mother Nature analytically decomposed exhibits an applied fractal process at the root. Elegant simplicity driving powerful results is the obvious consequence of good design and good programming within TBC.

Evolving a powerful, elegant, and simple fractral-like process to be the engine at the core, the motivating principle of reality, is the natural result of the Fundamental Process iterating toward optimal system solutions. It is the nature of all successful, large, and complex self-modifying systems to be constrained at the top level by elegant simplicity, otherwise chaos would destroy their viability. AUM and Mother Nature cannot help but reflect the fractal property of awesome complexity generated by the recursive application of elegant simplicity because that is how they themselves are constructed – they work as they are. Elegant simplicity is their secret, the key to evolving stable and productive complexity. For example, large social systems often fail (exhibit high entropy) because they lose the values (rule-set or constraints) that must provide a viable foundation for stable and productive evolution.

Toward the end of Chapter 20, Book 2 we discussed the concept of consciousness as a fractal system. There we saw that the **content** (as opposed to structure) of reality was derived from consciousness within consciousness within consciousness – computers within computers. From AUM to EBC to TBC to personal individuated consciousness in NPMR and PMR to human brains, to silicon based computers designing better silicon based computers, all reality appears to be populated and regulated within the form and structure of a giant fractal consciousness ecosystem. Each level of existence is derived from the consciousness above it by repeating the same basic attributes of consciousness on different scales and with differing form-functions. All entities are chips from the old AUM block at various levels and forms of being and awareness.

Digital consciousness, with its multitude of recursive interdependent expressions, is the engine at the core of reality – a fact that leads us to characterize consciousness as the father of all fractals.

The Fundamental Process of evolution permeates all reality as process within process within process, while consciousness provides the substance or self-organizing media upon which evolution's process operates. Gazillions of reality cells provide a conceptual digital media that can organize and reconfigure itself to lower its entropy, or equivalently, increase its useful energy. The Fundamental Process converts the potential for self-organization (potential digital energy) into aware brilliant love-consciousness. Our two basic assumptions given in Chapter 24, Book 1 – consciousness and evolution – can now be seen as the fundamental **substance** and **dynamics** of the larger reality – Father and Mother of All That Is.

Consciousness brings content, substance, value, potential energy, time, organization, and entropy while the Fundamental Process brings dynamics, structure, motion, change, profitability, and a process to convert potential mind into active mind by lowering entropy. Because that is all it takes to form reality, reality is nothing other than that. In all of its gazillions of forms and functions, from the most intricate superfine detail to the most global of overarching concepts, variations of these two fundamentals recursively repeated and applied at every possible scale, one level building upon the other, have produced All That Is. As in all fractals, a repetition of basic patterns and simple rules for change, applied recursively, yield a large, detailed, and complex result.

No doubt you have seen pictures of fractal images. Consider that the Big Picture is a Consciousness-Evolution fractal image. Think of our larger reality as an evolving mind-fractal. Do you see why **3D geometric** fractal images closely describe the natural objects within our **3D geometric** space-time reality? They are of a similar fractal nature and similar fractal type. Would not a fractal best and most accurately describe another fractal? It makes sense that a fractal reality constrained to **geometric** space-time (like PMR) could be described by geometric fractals.

Reality has a fractal nature because that is how it is built (evolved). Reality is a fractal, the result of a fractal process applied to the self organizing capacity of consciousness. AUM's conscious awareness, TBC, the space-time rule-set, and our beloved local PMR are generated by a recursive application of the Consciousness-Evolution fractal process. AUM, consciousness, and all reality are the result of the Consciousness-Evolution fractal propagating its way through the possibilities.

You not only live in a fractal reality and are a piece of a large digital fractal system, but you are a fractal component! Both the structural and the dynamic aspects of your individuated consciousness are part of a larger interactive pattern that we have called the greater consciousness ecosystem. This ecosystem (interactive interdependent system) is a complex consciousness-evolution fractal that is continually energized by applying the consciousness cycle to its self-evolving, self-organizing components. The virtual reality we experience as physical reality is simply a piece of that same fractal pattern. Carbon based biology; social systems, business, and political organizations; technology; and the non-sentient physical matter of PMR (trees, mountains, lakes, clouds) all express geometry-limited fractal characteristics in both form and content. We are all individuals, and are likewise made up of individual parts, but we, as well as our parts, are of the One Pattern – One Evolving Consciousness – all part and parcel of the Big-Fractal-Picture of Reality.

Once you get the idea of how one might generalize the fractal concept to include process and organization as well as geometry, it becomes clear that a reality based on the Fundamental Process of evolution working upon digital consciousness must necessarily result in a consciousness-evolution fractal, where consciousness is the reality media (the malleable substance to which the process is applied) and evolution is the process. PMR, being a component of such a reality, should have the word fractal written all over it – and it does. Governments, societies, cultures, businesses, economies, technology, people, critters, plants, mountains, forests, and rocks (as well as the ecologies each generates to sustain itself) are all created and driven to their present state through a fractal process of simple rules applied to a self-modifying complex system.

An evolving complex interactive system of consciousness is necessarily implemented as a process-fractal because consciousness can only interact with itself. Consciousness acting upon consciousness – pulling itself up by its own bootstraps through the replication of a simple process applied recursively at all available levels and scales where each new layer is built upon the previous one.

For every unique reality dimension, the profitability equation that drives its evolutionary process must reflect the rule-sets that constrain the possibilities within that reality dimension. Thus within OS, profitability requirements push consciousness toward lower entropy states while pushing PMR virtual matter toward lower energy states.

The Fundamental Process is the fundamental process; its profitability equation defines success; the environment applies the form factor; and space-time ensures consistency through the constraints defined by its rule-set. Realizing why geometric fractals accurately describe our 3D environment is just the beginning of understanding the fractal properties of our reality. Understanding the close connection between process fractals and ecosystems will eventually allow us to optimize our social, economic, cultural, organizational, and technological creations and institutions.

One needs to expand the limited concepts of ecology and ecosystem dynamics to include all systems of complex interdependent human activity (governments, societies, cultures, businesses, economies, technologies, and others). With a better understanding of process fractal dynamics we should be able to squeeze much entropy from the products of human organization. A better understanding of fractal ecosystems and the fractal nature of our reality will help create and define order within chaos.

To see the picture that I am painting one must expand their concepts of energy and evolution and realize that digital energy (the energy of organization created through entropy reduction) is not resource limited or limited to mass and fields, and that evolution is a fundamental process that applies to all self-modifying complex systems.

Once the Fundamental Process is better understood, it will become clear that we are surrounded by many critically important evolving systems that all follow the same simple process. Similarly, once the fractal nature of evolving systems is better understood, chaos will melt away into manageable and profitable processes. Furthermore, once the ecological model of evolving systems is better understood, human activities can become more efficient, cooperative, and productive on an ever greater scale.

To summarize, evolution defines the fundamental process, process fractals define the primary construction mechanism, and ecology defines the interactive structure of profitability. The techies in the audience should be reaching for their pencil sharpeners. Before them lies the opportunity of discovering the science of applied ecological fractals – a Big Picture approach to complex interactive systems analysis – which is timely and important because in the twenty-first century we all live, work, and play in a complex interactive world whose supporting systems are becoming more complex and interactive every year. What now appears random and chaotic from our little picture view is actually buttoned down and well behaved from the view of Big Picture fractal science.

Let's toss a TOE bone to the techies: Go boot up your computers and be the first on your block to invent a process fractal as well as a new academic discipline and an important new applied science, and you will be granted the rights to universal fame and three additional gold stars.

Rudimentary process fractals are already being applied by scientists investigating social and cultural dynamics in an effort to understand patterns of crime, ethnic segregation, and why the Anasazi abandoned northern Arizona 700 years ago. Although these elementary process fractals are constrained by exceedingly limited rule-sets, the artificial societies they model represent extremely complex results. (The simpler and shallower the rule-set the more likely it is that the process fractal will quickly converge to a steady state condition.) Using a process fractal to model a digital system dedicated to reducing its overall system entropy through evolution (self-improvement) will provide a rough simulation of our larger reality wherein the consciousness cycle will evolve as a winning strategy. Then, if the constraints of space-time are imposed to improve the efficiency of the consciousness cycle, we will find ourselves to be the result.

These are incredibly powerful and cool concepts. If you are unfamiliar with fractals, go look them up and find out what they are. After doing so, the Big Picture of our larger reality will suddenly make more intuitive sense. From the eye of a gnat, to a supernova, to the mechanics of NPMR, to AUM itself – all are expressions of a relatively simple consciousness-evolution interaction that repeats, copies, and clones itself at many levels and scales into a single magnificent fractal mental-image of digital existence. We are thus a simple but convoluted and recursive repetition of All That Is within All That Is. The greater consciousness ecosystem is a naturally occurring fractal system where each separately dimensioned habitat (virtual reality or dimension) reflects the fundamental pattern of evolving consciousness and is interconnected to, and dependant upon, the whole. Now, that's a Big Picture, but one that is within the grasp of our understanding.

Had I told you on page one that you are an individuated portion of a larger fractal pattern that constitutes All That Is within a digital virtual reality based upon evolving consciousness, you would have rolled your eyes and put the book back on the shelf. Hopefully, after you have finished rolling your eyes, you will at least allow this elegant concept to reside somewhere in a remote corner of your skeptical but open mind as you search for the personal experience-data that can confirm or deny its value and applicability.

You are a sentient entity designed primarily to evolve the quality of your being – the quality of your consciousness – because that is what one does in a Consciousness-Evolution fractal. That is the pattern of which you are a part. What else could you do as an individuated consciousness-evolution pattern subset existing within a consciousness-evolution fractal? Trying to do anything else, trying to break out of the pattern is futile – you are the pattern, the pattern is you – it is how you are defined. If you are unaware of this fact, you may be missing the point of your existence. You may be spending your time and energy in ways that are not important to your evolution, to your larger purpose within the larger reality. You are what you are – there is no point trying, or wishing, to be something else – you might as well learn how to play the game that you are in. There is no other game. If you get good at it, it is more enjoyable and more fun. Hanging out, clueless, in the middle of the playing field while others are fully engaged, having a blast, and making progress is a sad waste of your opportunity and of your potential.

The larger reality is not primarily a place defined (and bounded) by n-dimensional geometry where we live and objects exist, but rather a **process** for **becoming**, a process containing progressive (evolving) states of being – minimum energy for artillery rounds and elementary particles; minimum entropy for bright sentient entities such as you. The dynamics of the larger reality are driven by a process designed to facilitate the evolution of consciousness where individuals and the larger consciousness system mutually seek and find new end-states of higher profitability. The larger reality provides the opportunity for personal growth: the possibility of being all that you can be and more than you ever thought possible.

The N-Division piece of the larger consciousness ecosystem, reflects the fundamental nature of $NPMR_N$, requires local experiential subsystems (such as our PMR) of mass, space, time, and limited consciousness to serve as tools we can use to provide the opportunity for us to evolve through exercising free will choices. Why us? Why are we like that? Because consciousness evolving through the application of intent to free will choices reflects the repetitive pattern of our reality fractal. That is how consciousness and the Fundamental Process interact. We are provided the opportunity to apply the pattern of evolution to ourselves as an integral part of a larger process.

As with any seed, hologram, or fractal, the design of the whole is captured, expressed, and implemented within each part. The tiniest part (a neutrino, electron, or perhaps the intricate eye of the gnat) expresses the same Fundamental Process that represents and describes the universe, and beyond. This fundamental process of systems evolution is a process, within a process, within a process ... each tiny part containing the blueprint that drives, as well as explains, the whole.

You, both the physical and nonphysical you, are one small individual part that contains the essence, the pattern of the whole – an evolving individually-conscious piece of the larger evolving consciousness. You repetitively apply the Fundamental Process of evolution to yourself as you interact within your internal and external environments. You do the process, the process does you. You are a creator that exhibits, uses, and manipulates the evolution of consciousness and you are the result of that same process at both the nonphysical and physical levels. The Fundamental Process provides the dynamic principle that builds the structure, while consciousness provides the medium – the content, the fundamental energy, and organizational potential – that the process works upon. At the core is elegant simplicity, the hallmark of Big Truth.

No doubt there is much left to do and much left to understand. Nevertheless, is it not remarkable that one simple process and one simple energy form are all that is required to produce All That Is? Is it not remarkable that *My Big TOE* has been entirely and logically derived from only two simple assumptions – evolution and the potential energy of consciousness? Is it not remarkable that from these two assumptions a theory exhibiting elegant simplicity in form, structure, and application has seamlessly combined physics, metaphysics, ontology, epistemology, and cosmology to answer many questions of science, philosophy, and theology (both ancient and modern) that have gone begging for answers for years? Is it not intellectually and emotionally satisfying that the full and complete answers to these historically unanswerable questions turn out to be relatively simple, straightforward, and logically concise once old paradigms are generalized to provide a more accurate perspective of the nature of our reality?

Do you see how the application of this Big TOE makes the fundamentals of life, science, philosophy, and metaphysics easier to understand and more obvious to apply and use, while driving nothing to greater complication or obscuration? Big Truth simplifies issues and understanding – it never complicates. On the other hand, beliefs (as do lies) require an ever greater complexity to support them as they spread and grow. None of what we scientists have worked so hard and long to understand has to be discarded – only relegated to a subset of a larger, more comprehensive understanding.

You, I, and the dog next door are of one consciousness, one source one connected evolutionary pattern. Nevertheless, every level of existence has its own mission and purpose. We sentient beings in OS have our mission, our reason and purpose for being. That mission requires that we have free will and the ability to interact freely with other individuated conscious-ness within the constraints of our experience and the quality of our unique fragment of consciousness. This arrangement provides us with the maximum opportunity to evolve our consciousness, our being, and our quality according to the pattern or our larger reality.

> ▶ "Hey Jake! Put that stupid toe-book down and bring in the cooler while I turn on the tube! Wrestling's coming on! Can you believe it? The 'Mad Menace' is going up against 'Killer Mc Bee' in a grudge match – that ought to be really good!
> If 'The Bee' gets his stinger out, man, there will be blood everywhere. That would be so cool! The last time he got banned for three months – remember? And Jake, listen to this – hey, pop me a cool one, pal – after the main event they are going to let the women wrestle. I don't know their names but I got a good look at 'em on the pre-match interviews and one of them has really big…" ◀

Improving the quality of consciousness, advancing the quality and depth of awareness, understanding your nature and purpose, maturation of soul, manifesting universal unconditional love, letting go of fear, and eliminating ego, desire, wants, needs, or preconceived notions – these are the attributes and the results of a successfully evolving consciousness. What do the facts of your life, the facts of your existence, and your results say about the quality of your consciousness, the effectiveness of your process, or the size of your picture?

Progress is measured only by results – clear obvious results. There are no quality points given for good effort or nice try or for believing or not believing anything. You are an in-charge (of your opportunities) respon-sible adult individuated consciousness. You cannot bribe, cheat, fake out, or hustle the system. There is no spiritual welfare system. There are no shortcuts. You have to do it 100% by yourself and your friends, connec-tions, and cash cannot help you. Excuses earn zero credit irrespective of how well justified they are. Only results earn credit.

On the other hand, there is no practical time limit – you can take as long as you want or need to. There is generally no such thing as absolute failure – failure is relative and simply equates to a lack of progress. There are no exits, no escapes, no way out or around, except through personal growth.

If you think that you may have gained some new knowledge or insight in the process of comparing Big TOEs with me, I must remind you that with knowledge comes responsibility.

I thought you would want to know.

14

■■■

Section 5 Postlude
Hail! Hearty Readers, Thou Hast
Completed Nonphysical Mechanics 101

■■■

If you have made it this far without skipping over too much of the more difficult material and have let the concepts presented in Section 2, 3, 4 and 5 intermingle and bounce around inside your skeptical but open mind, you have earned my respect and appreciation regardless of what you think about what you have read.

Now that you understand the Big Picture evolutionary process of improving the quality of your consciousness by making choices based on right motivation, simple things such as the point of your existence and the meaning of your life should be obvious. You should, by this point in our journey, have a good idea of where you came from, where you are, where you need to go, and how to get started on the journey to get there. Hopefully, you will remember not to confuse reality with the model of reality.

No doubt, a few readers are struggling to justify their old and comfortable paradigms. For the most part, their justifications, though familiar and traditional, are neither logical nor objective, but appear, from their view, to be both. Wrestling old paradigms and beliefs to the ground is exceptionally difficult to do. To be a lonely warrior in a strange land requires more courage and personal strength than is commonly available. By having almost completed this trilogy, you have proved yourself to possess uncommon fortitude, strength, and courage as well as plenty of extra time.

For some, stepping off the well-beaten path brings up deep seated anxieties – the unknown, the non-conforming, and the unaccepted strike fear deep into the hearts of those in need of reassurance. So it is with all social (herd) animals – and so it shall always be – it is their fundamental nature to seek safety in numbers and in conformity to norms. Beware: In a fearful stampede to save themselves from the terrifying menace of an original idea, the herd can become a mindless destroyer of the light. This is simply how it is: **No fault or error is implied**.

For bravery, courage, and outstanding stamina, I do hereby grant you permission to paste four additional shiny gold stars in your book. Congratulations! Thine treasure of unearthly gold doth greatly grow.

Unfortunately, many readers find at this point that they need to read Sections 2, 3, 4, and 5 again to pull it all together in their heads. At first reading, the introduction of so many new and unusual concepts keeps your head spinning and often causes philosophical discombobulation, existential confusion, metaphysical vertigo, as well as belief-trap withdrawals. These in turn inhibit Big Picture conceptual coalescence. It is a sad fact of life that much of what you read in earlier sections will make more sense now that you have completed Section 5.

Isn't that how it always is? You are properly prepared to take a difficult course – and thoroughly learn the material – only after you have finished struggling through it for the first time. Unfortunately, we almost never retake a course because we are in too big a hurry to begin struggling through the next one. I am reminded of the office maxim: There is never enough time to do it right, but always enough time to do it again. That rings especially true when your view of time spans multiple lifetimes.

The next and final Section (Section 6) is a short wrap-up that will help you put what you have been exposed to during the previous four sections into a more personal and balanced perspective. You are now on the downhill slope of the Big TOE thrill-a-minute ride into your consciousness – only a little more effort is required and you will be entitled to brag to your friends that you were able to get through the entire thing – from shaft to knuckle to nail. Though they will, no doubt, be envious of your new twinkling stars, you should begin thinking about what you are going to tell them when they ask you what these books are all about, what you learned, and whether or not contemplating your Big TOE is as fun, interesting, and useful as it sounds.

▶ At the very least, if you can think of nothing else to say, you can change the subject by firmly asserting the undisputable fact: that during meditation, your big toe is always easier to see than your navel. With sustained concentration being an immensely difficult thing for most people, your navel challenged friends will immediately see the advantage and think you clever to have penetrated the infamous belly-button barrier and obviated the nuisance of propping up mirrors all in one ingenious stroke. Ahhhh ha! So that's why they pull their feet up on their knees like that! Now I get it! It's the big toe, stupid!

Shhhhh, whisper! This is a great secret of the Mystic Inner Circle, don't blab it all around. Nobody is supposed to know why we sit like that and wear open toed sandals year-round. Think of it my friend, through your clever choice of offbeat dubious reading material, you have discovered the ancient mystical key to the door of enlightenment – your friends will no doubt be mightily impressed. One more thing, please, do not tell anybody that I told you this. If you must tell, use someone else's name – I knew I could count on you – thanks. If it is found out that I have let this secret slip out, ancient dis-embodied Tibetan warriors will come to the foot of my bed at night and tickle my feet. Oh jeez, a fate worse than life! ◀

We will regroup at the beginning of Section 6 in the morning where you will receive your final set of briefings before going off on your own into whatever reality you have thus far created for yourself. It is time to think about what comes next – and what, if anything, reality has to do with you. The most significant questions for you to ponder are: Just how real are you really? How aware are you of awareness and how large a larger reality can you stand to understand?

In Section 6, I provide the perspective with which you can sum up everything you have been exposed to on this trip through Big-TOE-land. Perhaps you will begin to formulate a strategy for where you want to go next – and how you might get there. After Section 6, the ball is in your court – and you will need to figure out what the game is, and how to play to win. This is the last inning pal, get some sleep and be ready to go at sun-up – this time we will not wait for stragglers.

Section 6

■ ■ ■

The End is Always the Beginning: Today is the First Day of the Rest of Your Existence

■ ■ ■

15

■■■

Introduction to Section 6

■■■

You can secure a major advance in Big Picture understanding by merely appreciating your ignorance within a larger point of view, even if your experience allows no perceptible conversion of that ignorance into knowledge. Learning begins when you are capable of appreciating your ignorance enough to ask a question and care about the quality of the answer. When you know or believe you know the right answer, learning is not possible.

We are not children. Simply asking the question is not enough. There is no Mom, or Dad, or organization capable of supplying us with an easy answer that is also a quality answer. A quality answer is one that is part of your personal solution without also being part of your personal problem.

One of the most obvious Big-questions left hanging in thought-space after reading *My Big TOE* is: What now? I think that is a good question – it may be less obvious, but I have that same question. What, if anything, are you going to do with the ideas and concepts you have encountered in *My Big TOE*? That is my question. Perhaps you will be willing to share your answer with me and others at: **http://www.my-big-toe.com**.

Unfortunately, if you are to reach significant conclusions about the content of *My Big TOE* you will need to either build some bridges or jump to them across a chasm of ignorance and ingrained belief. How many bridges and how much distance they must span is dependent on the breadth, depth, and quality of your experience data and the size and shape of your personal chasm.

Building logically and scientifically sound bridges from carefully evaluated experience is always a more difficult methodology for reaching conclusions than jumping to them, but if you want to progress beyond chasing your tail it is absolutely necessary. We think puppies and kittens are

funny when they are in full and ardent pursuit of their tail for a few seconds at a time. Imagine how funny a human must look dedicating its
entire life to a self-referential endless loop of non-productive tail chasing.
Actually it is more sad than funny, but these are the typical views when
looking from the perspective of the Big Picture.

To help you decide what to do about the ideas and concepts you have
encountered in *My Big TOE*, I have compiled six suggestions for your considered action in reverse order of difficulty. 1) Do not throw good after
bad – drop these ideas out of your mind like hot (or rotten) potatoes –
use the books to warm yourself this winter, or give them to some mushy-
brained acquaintance you wish to irritate. 2) After some initial excite-
ment, forget about the Big Picture – it is too big to do anything about anyway. The ideas presented, though intellectually interesting, will naturally
drift away as you pour yourself into the next activity, and the next one
after that. 3) Because you are reading it only for the t-shirt, go to the
http://www.my-big-toe.com web site and see if you can procure an official
Big TOE t-shirt. After all, you did read the entire book and have the
empty aspirin bottles and 17 shiny gold stars to prove it. For that alone,
this renegade wordsmith owes you – big time! 4) Send a fiery letter full
of indignation and well-placed exclamation marks to the publisher
requesting them to cease and desist from further polluting the accumulated knowledge base with mindless drivel. Insist your letter be forwarded
to the author at his home in Antarctica. 5) In a bubble bursting with fresh
enthusiasm, decide to get someone (book, class, seminar, guru) to help
you develop the results of your personal Big Picture understanding before
sooner or later returning to 2) above. 6) Do not throw good after bad –
commit serious time and energy to a lifelong skeptical but open minded
personal pursuit of Big Truth – and go energetically wherever that path
might lead. Become a pudding-head on the path to true love.

Any of the above six choices (and countless others) are acceptable: you
must move in a direction that **appears** to be forward from wherever you
are and from whatever perspective you have accumulated thus far. You
make choices, and the choices you make, make you. Free will is the driver.
Choices and consequences, reaping what you sow, getting what you
deserve, and deserving what you get – that is how the game is played –
lose or win. All individuals are equally important and valuable, and all
choices are valid steps along your path of being, whether you know what
you are doing or not.

My advice to you and hopes for you have nothing to do with which of
the six choices you settle on – whichever choice represents who you are

today **can eventually** take you where you need to go tomorrow. My advice and hope is that you will choose only after careful consideration and that you will constantly reevaluate whatever choice you make as the evidence of your lifetime dribbles in.

16

■ ■ ■

I Can't Believe I Read the Whole Thing
Uncle Tom, Pass the Antacid Please

■ ■ ■

*M*y *Big TOE* was written to allow me to share the tentative results of my explorations with you. It is in the style of a personal conversation between you and your eccentric Dutch uncle – strange old Uncle Tom. The informal tone and use of humor reflects how I normally relate, one-on-one, with good friends who want to know, and whose eyes have not yet begun to glaze over. This approach is calculated to maintain interest and to minimize the wow and gee whiz effects.

I could have made a more serious, formal, erudite presentation that would have been much more intellectually impressive – like the typical book authored by some hot-shot scientist from the prestigious University of Tough Love with an impressive string of cryptic letters after his name. Something like this: Dr. Uncle Tom, B.S., I.M.S., Ur.D. where BS is self-explanatory and S and D imply smart and dumb respectively – at least that's the message intentionally left lurking between the lines. Trying to be impressive or worse yet, seeing yourself as actually being impressive is, in the Big Picture, equivalent to having a lobotomy.

Contrary to popular belief, you do not have to be a doctor, lawyer, executive, high ranking military officer, government manager, politician, or university professor to get a lobotomy – but if you are one of these supremely impressive individuals, you get to go immediately to the front of the line, no questions asked. Don't giggle, that is no small advantage – there is always a very long line at Lobotomy Central.

Appearing impressive is something you should always carefully **avoid** – even if you must act a little silly sometimes. Silly mixed in equal measure with down-home and funky is always a sure winner in the "oh, it's only you" sweepstakes. Avoiding actually being impressive is exceedingly simple for most of us while avoiding the appearance of being impressive requires a more concentrated effort on our part.

It is important that you do not take the attitude that serious progress along the Path of Knowledge is only available to the special few. That it is beyond your practical reach – only for robed gurus who dedicate their life to the pursuit of spiritual perfection or Ph.D. physicists who are so far out in the esoteric ether that even they have no idea what they are talking about. Nothing could be further from the truth. You can succeed superbly without changing your outward life-style very much. You should know that I am a regular down-to-earth guy with a job, a wife, young kids, multiple dogs, birds, marsupials and snakes; one cat, two old cars, a whopping mortgage, and last but not least, a very strange sense of humor.

Personal spiritual progress does not require disengagement; it does not require a high and lofty demeanor, or a serious superior-to-thou attitude. Clearly, those attributes indicate a **lack** of spiritual progress, a **deficiency** of consciousness quality. Unfortunately, people have a natural tendency to place those they think know more than they do on a pedestal – and denigrate their own worth or progress by comparison. This is a belief trap that makes progress much less likely. You will evolve more quickly by tossing out the Great Guru and seriously working on your own, than by hanging out with the Great Guru in lieu of doing serious work on your own. Quality of consciousness is, for the most part, not gained through association or by osmosis.

Placing others on pedestals is nonproductive and makes **you** feel less competent by comparison. Do not fall into this energy and incentive destroying belief trap.

Natural and simple processes usually work the best. It is my hope that being "one of us" in language and style will reach more folks than informal and corny will lose. I am betting on the likelihood that many people will listen more openly and less defensively to their Dutch uncle. More importantly, it is clear that the minimum number of readers will get trapped by the wow effect if the delivery is straightforward, humorous, and informal. That gives the uncle-dude a more effective place from which to communicate and share whatever I think might be of value to you.

Those turned-off or lost for want of a serious, intellectual, top expert demeanor are probably too far gone into the depths of ego and self-referential belief traps to get much from *My Big TOE* anyway. It all works out. What you end up with is: Funky Physics for the Rest of Us – a personal tour through reality with your Dutch uncle. I hope the style, tone, and humor was as good for you as it was for me. Self-important professional stuffed shirts and pompous professor types will need to descend to a more common level to ferret out the few Big TOE golden nuggets that happen to be color coordinated with their egos and career goals. If that is too painful a condescension, they can always watch TV instead.

Looking and acting normal and being normal can be two separate things. The point is: You can seriously and successfully pursue the Path of Knowledge, the path of consciousness quality evolution, of spiritual development and continue to carry on with your normal life. Sure, there will be lots of changes, but none that require you to step dramatically out of your lifestyle as an **initial** investment in future growth. The quality and evolution of your consciousness is not dependent on the **form** of your physical existence. However, the **quality** of your physical existence depends absolutely on the quality of your consciousness.

Because most, if not all, of the people we know who are successfully pursuing a spiritual path or path of personal growth are not normally immersed in our Western techno-culture, we **believe** incorrectly that family, jobs, and mortgages are incompatible with a serious bid for enlightenment (understanding and living the Big Picture at a deep level). Likewise, because we have a small, half-formed picture of what consciousness quality or spiritual progress means, we **believe** that dropping out of the mainstream (becoming monks, priests, nuns, living in solitary places, joining spiritually focused organizations, performing rituals, wearing funny clothes, or severing material connections) must be required: They are not.

The **form** of your material involvement with the local reality is not important. How you interact with that environment, how you relate with others, what you make of the available choices and opportunities – that is important – and that can be done anywhere under a wide range of circumstances that includes Western culture and lifestyles. Do not let these two belief traps (the wow-effect and the drop-out blues) discourage you from setting out on a quest to evolve the quality of your consciousness.

When you hear others use these erroneous beliefs as excuses for why they cannot successfully pursue a more spiritual path, first shout: Copout!, and then, Bullpucky! Next, apologize for your rude uncontrolled outburst. Finally, explain with great empathy and compassion why nothing is required to change but them, and that creating the right environment **first** typically retards progress by inadvertently putting the cart in front of the horse, causing energy to be focused on issues of minor importance. Successful learning does not flow from the right environment – the right environment flows from successful learning. The environment that is most important with regards to your growth is the one in your head. The appropriate physical environment will form on its own.

The West, unlike the East, has not evolved its own distinct cultural processes to support the evolution of individual consciousness. When and if it does, dropping out of the mainstream will not be a requirement. In the West, neither our religious nor our secular processes are designed to help individuals outgrow the belief traps that dramatically limit their potential growth. To the contrary, our Western institutions foster, support, and demand, an array of limiting beliefs with great gusto. The same is true in Eastern cultures.

Westerners are especially proud of their logical and scientific ways. That Western attitudes and processes are often belief based and not as logical and scientific as they appear to us through our tinted cultural glasses, is obvious to many who live outside Western culture.

Nevertheless, the Path of Knowledge, the warrior's path, the relentless pursuit of truth, the application of logic and the intellect in the service of consciousness evolution are right down our Western alley. Progress on the Path of Knowledge depends upon rational process. Rational process is where the Western worldview supposedly shines – the one thing Western culture prides itself on more than any other. We of the West thrive on rational process. In fact, we are so obsessively committed to rational process that everything we do is construed to be the result of a rational process whether it is or not. We simply define it to be that way! If we do it, we can somehow justify it as a rational and logical process; at least the men can, the ladies often know better.

Ahhh...so close, yet so far away! A decided spiritual advantage lies unseen and thus unused. The Path of Knowledge is not well worn by Western feet. We of Western attitude live with and enjoy the material advantages, regret or do not see the spiritual disadvantages, and for the most part entirely miss the spiritual advantages. Every culture has its advantages and disadvantages. Because you must live with **all** the disadvantages of your culture, it is a shame to allow self-imposed belief-blindness to deny you access to some of your culture's more significant advantages.

Hopefully, *My Big TOE* has occasionally prodded you out of your habitual no-brainer comfort zone, or at least challenged your mind with a few new concepts. Perhaps you have taught yourself a thing or two in the process of struggling with the unusual ideas found here. That you end up agreeing, disagreeing, or better yet undecided, is not important. That there was some mental motion, some stirring about within an open mental space – **that is** important – and if the motion, the seeking, continues for a long time, that is even more important.

Whether or not **your** Big TOE is correct or flawed, diminutive or great, is also not important as long as it is moving you in the right general direction. Because an individual's Big TOE must be perpetually in a state of growth, improvement, and evolution, the motion part is easy. Maintaining your heading in the correct general direction is also easy for committed, honest pudding tasters. If you start growing **a** big TOE and continually progress it in the right general direction, you will eventually end up with **the** Big TOE; that is why it is more important to get serious and get going than it is to make sure you are doing it absolutely right. From the perspective of PMR, the process of reducing entropy within your consciousness has many valid approaches. It is a naturally convergent process that will take you from wherever you are to where you need to be. Regardless of what direction you initially take, if you are serious and persistent, you will eventually end up with the same result. Some paths are simply more or less efficient depending on the individual.

The important thing is to start. Your understanding does not need to be perfect as long as it is constantly and consistently converging on rightness. That your Big TOE enables **you** to focus **your** energy on the task of growing toward a higher quality of consciousness is the critical ingredient of eventual success. Your constantly updated Big TOE should be the central part of your continual process of converging on perfection, correctness, enlightenment, and love.

If reading *MY Big TOE* has caused you to grapple with your beliefs in the context of a larger reality and induced you to come to **any** helpful tentative conclusions about the quality and purpose of your life, it has been a great success from my view. However, if you agree completely with everything in *My Big TOE* but do not gain momentum or understanding that helps you to improve the quality of your consciousness, then this trilogy has helped you focus your experience, or simply entertained you; in either case there is little significance. If that is your case, I can only hope that I have left a spark of interest or understanding that will produce flames later on. For those who agree and disagree with *My Big TOE*, if no spark of greater knowledge or no flame for seeking truth is carried away, I have wasted your time. The information in *My Big TOE* is meant to be news that you can use, not chatter splatter for New-Age groupies or PMR apologists.

I have had loads of fun hanging out with you for the last several weeks or months, or however long it has taken you to get this far. We have covered a lot of new conceptual ground together and have had some laughs in the process. If you have read the entire trilogy and are still hanging with me in this quest to see the Big Picture and develop a comprehensive model of reality – and to find your place in it – I expect that you have what it takes to go the distance. You are among the few to whom I hope to make a significant difference.

You may find this difficult to believe, but some who started on this journey with us, including a few who approached *My Big TOE* with serious open minded intent, became and remain frustrated to the max. Many of these didn't make it past Section 2 or Section 3 because of the high levels of frustration – a natural filter that you passed through with flying colors.

Why all this frustration and angst? Because I emphasize repetitively that it is up to you to go out and get evidence for yourself and come to your own conclusions. Add that to the fact that I constantly reminded you that your growth is critical to the quality of life you experience and to your evolutionary progress. Furthermore, I am forever pointing out the purpose of your existence and emphasizing the importance of your success (in the little picture and the Big Picture) in fulfilling that purpose and that you alone must assume full responsibility for your success or failure.

Additionally, I make it clear there is precious little help within PMR to aid your success, and that a long term focused effort is required to pull yourself up by your bootstraps one tiny increment at a time. On top of all this tough love I am continually insinuating that you are probably not as spiritually evolved as you think or hope that you are; that you are more than likely driven by ego, wants, desires, and fear; and that your existence is probably not as close to the center of the reality-universe as you may have imagined. Wow! What a trip ... and that's the good news!

Frustration accrues because although I provide some technique and direction on how to get started, there are no guarantees of immediate success and few hints about what to do after you do get started. I am not holding out on you, or being vague to get you to read my next book, or avoiding the issue because I don't know the answer – it is simply that growing-up is something that no one else can tell you how to do.

Your mother and your boss can tell you how to **act**, but only you can decide how to **be**. Unfortunately, acting properly (exhibiting proper behavior and intellectual understanding) without proper being, though civilizing, is of little value in raising the quality of your consciousness. Getting into a learning process that is significantly ahead or behind your grade level is more counterproductive than helpful: Boredom and frustration are terrific inhibitors of actualizing potential. Mass marketed materials are not the right media for effectively guiding an individual's personal growth.

I could, if I had little understanding and even fewer scruples, try to convince you that I possess the knowledge of a sure path to greater spiritual quality and then sell it to you on the side in the form of books, tapes, lectures, seminars, and training courses, but that would be more marketing bullpucky than truth. There is no short cut that significantly minimizes the work you must do on your own. There are many equally valid paths. You should choose one that fits your demeanor, style, and situation. None of them can give you anything but an **opportunity** for you to do the work required to improve yourself. Promises of anything more are empty and generally made by those more interested in the quality of your bank account than in the quality of your consciousness.

My Big TOE is not a how-to book, nor is it an advanced tome on better living through physics and meditation – it is simply a Reality 101 survey course – just enough information to get you started on your own adventure of discovery. How-to instructions, to be effective, must be individually focused and personally delivered: A one-size-fits-all book is not a good media for teaching individuals how to experience the larger reality. A book may teach you useful meditation techniques (see Chapter 23, Book 1), but it intrinsically has a difficult time helping you interpret and understand (guide) your personal meditation experiences. How useful is the former without the latter? For the large majority, not much. Typically, such a book will serve only to shift the point of terminal frustration from a pre-meditation, "I do not know how to get started," to a post-meditation, "My experiences are indefinable, uncontrollable, and without specific meaning."

The first type of frustration: Enthusiasm constrained by ignorance, has a long half-life, and may eventually lead to real progress if the enthusiasm can overcome the constraints of the ignorance before it decays. The second: I've done that and it doesn't appear to lead anywhere, has a much shorter half-life, rarely leads to real progress, and makes it less likely that the individual will ever make real progress. The second type of frustration is not always, or necessarily, the result of an unguided effort. Certain bright, dogged, robust individuals, who are ready to learn, dive right in and, with little to no guidance, become great swimmers in the crystal clear waters of the larger reality. Unfortunately, these individuals are rare; the rest essentially do a belly-flop, spend their life doggie paddling around in circles, or get out of the water permanently.

An immediate concern of mine is that this trilogy, because it is targeted at a broad base of readers, might do more harm than good by encouraging an epidemic of the belly-flop blues. That is a downside risk I accept in order to offer the upside potential of stimulating significant new growth.

The perseverance, effort, and lack of ego required for dramatic success act as a natural filter to cull out those who are not ready to access the greater power and responsibility of an aware consciousness. Balance and stability are inherent to the process.

The rare few who are powerfully driven, sans ego, to find answers will find a way – they always do – they need only to see the possibilities; it is never easy, but for them, easy is not required.

In terms of learning about being, we in the West have a learning disability built into our cultural values. Our model of education employs an intellectual process designed for stuffing facts into the student's head. Learning to be is necessarily an experiential process, not an intellectual process. Much of our frustration derives from wanting to achieve the latter (learning to be, growing-up, evolving our consciousness) by employing the former (intellectual process). We push and push on that intellectual string until we give up in exasperation and conclude that the larger reality is either inaccessible to us or simply does not exist.

Babies do not learn to walk or speak by thinking about it, being told about it, logically analyzing it, or having it explained to them – it takes only a **dim glimmer** of the possibilities and great courage and determination. *My Big TOE* is trying as hard as it can to supply the dim glimmer; you must supply the courage and determination.

Feeling frustrated because the solution is not one you can get an intellectual grip on or intellectually master is futile unless the frustration drives you to continue trying until you become a consciousness toddler. A valiant and ardent search for the right intellectual understanding, the right intellectual tools, process, procedures, directions, recipe, or prescription is a search in vain. The key you are looking for does not exist in intellectual or physical form. There is no recipe, syllabus, outline, book, or set of instructions that holds the answer for you because this is not an intellectual exercise. This fact is extremely difficult for a product of modern Western education to understand.

Finally, if you are discomforted or irritated by hearing me continually infer that you probably have a long way to go and a lot of work to do, consider the use of the carrot and the stick. Providing the dim glimmer is a carrot and stick process; nothing else works. Carrots without sticks are less irritating than sticks without carrots but neither approach will produce any smart mules. To encourage your personal journey of discovery, I have scattered a few enticing carrots here and there throughout the previous five sections. It is also possible that you received a whack or two with a humorstick that was hand crafted from your ego. It is my intention that the application of sticks should be more of a gentle poke or helpful nudge than a whack. However, I am fully aware that one person's nudge is often another person's whack. A sudden or forceful growing up typically appears to be harsh.

If *My Big TOE* has left you feeling frustrated or disconcerted, it may be because the truth often does not fit comfortably into our established routines and belief systems, and that we often do not want to hear what our intuition is trying to tell us. Not knowing for sure whether Uncle Tom is absolutely correct, nuts, or hopelessly lost, is irrelevant to your personal growth. Not starting on a journey of discovery to find answers because you lack answers is a self-defeating deception of the ego aimed at denying fear and reducing anxiety. Embrace uncertainty: You cannot know where your path will take you. Plan only life's journey, not life's destination. Accept that you are always more ignorant of your ignorance than you think. Do not let the heights of your uncertainty, the depths of your ignorance, or the importance of your mission intimidate you.

I have discovered that most readers like Section 1 the best. Most like my descriptions of NPMR, comments about the Big Cheese, and at least a few of the jokes. Many also enjoy Uncle Tom poking fun at self-important stuffed shirts and iconoclastically tweaking the nose of brain-dead dogmatists. In general, people like to hear about the critters I've met, nonphysical sex, gender identification in NPMR, and stories of the epic adventures and conflicts that are taking place within the larger reality. Some are fascinated by how things work in NPMR and the interaction between PMR and NPMR. These stories, anecdotes, and descriptions are interesting to most everyone because they are not challenging (no conceptual heavy lifting is required) and because they have great entertainment value.

One attribute that makes entertainment so popular is that it occurs at a distance – the one being entertained does not have to participate or get personally involved. Being entertained is a pleasant, safe, secure, comfortable intellect-at-a-distance activity that requires little effort, carries no responsibility, and therefore generates no fear, guilt, potential for failure, or personal growth. By vicariously reading about (or watching) others doing amazing or cool things, we are able to share and confirm the hero's reality in terms of our own reality without the effort or risk.

Our own possibilities are thus **theoretically** expanded. That's not all bad, but the limitations are obvious.

I could spin stories of adventures, battles, and intrigues in NPMR that would keep you interested and spellbound until you decided that I must be nuts. This is what most people want me to talk about most of the time – all useless, except for its entertainment value. Entertainment value is highly coveted in the marketplace, but it is better at developing cash-flow than it is at developing consciousness.

▶ News or 'truth' as entertainment – that is the tabloid approach – and the rest of our mainstream news producers are in that same boat or headed there in a big hurry – they are merely less obvious. We the people are driving the content of all mass marketed information to that same sad state of affairs. The dynamics are simple: 1) Information distribution is a business and must sell to remain competitive and profitable; 2) People prefer to be entertained; and, 3) The truth is not in big demand.

Likewise, people often prefer a tabloid approach to reality as well. (See the aside within the aside near the middle of Chapter 24, Book 1.) Unfortunately, little to no improvement in the quality of your consciousness can be achieved by listening to other people's experiences because making meaningful improvements (consciousness evolution) is **not** an intellectually-driven process. Quite the contrary: Personal growth is an intent, free will, choice making, choice executing, consequence assessing, pudding tasting, experience-driven process.

Gather 'round folks, I am about to blab a rare heart-felt confession. I am not interested in entertaining you with my experiences in NPMR because there is little potential value in it. Actually, it is worse than that; the down side is significantly greater than the upside. Interesting and exciting tales from the Big Picture serve mainly to distract your focus from what you ought to be paying attention to. Spiritual growth through entertainment sounds as dumb as it is. Improvement in your consciousness quality must flow from your own direct experience. Intellectual analysis cannot generate new experience. Enough said. ◀

The experience of others can provide only a tentative bigger view of the possibilities – it may provide some direction, but it cannot move you forward toward greater personal quality by even a single small step. You must learn to recognize what is mainly entertainment and not confuse it with those experiences that could directly lead toward personal growth. It is not always as easy as it initially appears to make that discrimination, but until you can tell the difference and act accordingly, you will remain in square one.

Entertainment is undeniably what the marketplace wants, but that is not my interest, function, or intent in creating this trilogy. You already have a huge array of choices if entertainment and quick spiritual fixes are what you are pursuing. Here, you are expected to do your own serious iterative thinking and experiencing in order to come to your own tentative conclusions.

You now know some of the considerations and dynamics that shaped the writing of *My Big TOE*. I made you wait until almost the end so you wouldn't be tempted to second-guess my presentation and delivery. The inside scoop divulged in this chapter is reserved for my favorite readers – those who were tough enough, interested enough, and determined enough to make it (almost) all the way to the end.

▶ Now you know: *The Untold Secrets Behind MY Big TOE.* (How's that for an oxymoronic tabloid headline?) Or, how about this: *Uncle Tom – Exposed!* People would love it, and sadly, find it more believable if Uncle Tom turned out to be an ancient Egyptian wizard accidentally raised from the dead by leaky radioactive waste. What is the real story behind *MY Big TOE?* When a senior editor at a small publishing house read an early version of the manuscript, he called me to ask, "Where did you get all this stuff?" Would you believe I teleported here from a spaceship that remains hidden on the dark side of the moon just to implant these words of wisdom into the collective consciousness of the pathetically inferior but nonetheless deserving earthlings, so that eventually they might become worthy of contact by my people?

OK, OK, this is the real, true, truth: My name really is Tom, and I am (or at least used to be) The Big Cheese's favorite Uncle. The unvarnished truth is that The Big Cheese sent me here because I beat him three times in a row in the heavyweight lightning bolt hurl. That is a fact – three times! Nobody had ever done that before. I know in my heart of hearts that he sent me to this clueless humanoid-hell-hole to get even, but what he said was…let me give you the exact quote… "Uncle Tom, see if you can help those bone-headed earthlings get their shit together." That is exactly what he said, word for word, honest! Jeez, I worked on designs for outhouses, flush toilets, and sewage treatment plants for almost 2,700 years before I figured out that I was supposed to write these damn books!

This is tons of fun, and I am tempted to go on and on, but let's get to the point. Many people would find *My Big TOE* more credible, much easier to take seriously, and less threatening if its origins were fantastical (as above), accidental (the result of being bonked on the head by a meteorite), or the words of a mysterious and mystical individual – perhaps a monk that has been in a cave for thirty years or a super-duper guru from a foreign culture. Why? Those sources are easy to keep at an ego-safe distance because they have nothing to do with us personally; they imply no responsibility on our part. ◀

▶▶ "If this so-called enlightened man is just like us, then he couldn't know that much more than we do. Right? If he is, and he does, we should be able to do the same thing. Right? Well, then, why haven't we?

"The unmistakable conclusion is that either he is non-credible, or we are failures, or at least have come up very short in actualizing our potential. Intellect, please tell me which possibility is the one I should believe.

"My ego and intellect agree that I have done all I can reasonably do. Whew, I feel better already. I knew that he was too ordinary and just like me to know that much more than I do.

"There for a minute, I felt small, fragmented, and insecure; like I needed to refocus my life completely, but now I am whole and in charge again.

"Too bad Mr. Know-it-all didn't pan out; I wish that he possessed the truth and insight that I have been seeking these many years. He is, it turns out, at worst a hustler, or at best simply confused – what an ego in either case! The world is full of people like him who think they know **the** answer. I have listened to them all, but none of them have ever **done** anything for me. I remain the same. Perhaps a few of the more popular ones have part of the answer, but none seems to have the entire answer. I am beginning to think that knowing the entire answer is impossible, that life is meant to remain mysterious, that we can never know the larger truth. If nobody really knows, or can know, the answers to life's hardest questions, then I am doing as well as can be expected and better than most.

"Surely, we all agree, one must be exceedingly careful about who and what to believe.

"Nevertheless, I must continue my search for The One who knows the truth, The One that will share the truth with me so that I too can become enlightened. Perhaps the next Mr. Know-it-all (they seem to come and go all the time) will be the real one – the one who will set my spirit free!

"I have tried it all. My hopes soar with every new process or teacher. Nonetheless, my spiritual quest seems to wander aimlessly with little real progress. All the enlightened gurus are totally inaccessible. I can't quit my job and family to hang out with some guru – that would not be responsible or right. Maybe there is no way to get to there from here?

"I wonder if I am doing something wrong. If I could only meet an enlightened person who was accessible, who could relate to me, who understood my needs and commitments – someone more like me." ◀◀

▶ Is that guy lost or what? His almost total irrationality is derived from belief trap piled upon belief trap until only the twisted framework of a bizarre self-apparent logic remains. I counted at least twenty-eight unique belief traps piled one upon the other – how many did you see? Unfortunately, not much forward progress is likely for this particular tail-chasing seeker of spiritual truth until he learns to break out of the endless loop of Catch-22s he has created for himself.

It is a simple fact that everyone has the **potential** to learn what I have learned, experience what I have experienced, and do what I can do. It may take significant effort and dedication, but it doesn't have to disrupt your life very much. This fact is deeply discomforting to the ego. Rather than jump for joy at the possibilities, a much more common response is to shrink from the personal implications and to deny personal responsibility. One always finds it easier to generate excuses than to generate results.

If my knowledge were the result of being hit by tiny meteorite fragments (dust), contact with an alien, falling off a ladder, or channeling the material directly from god himself, you would have a ready-made excuse. The material is clearly beyond your practical knowing. You can do no more than choose whether to **believe** it or not. There can be no blame, no self-expectation, and no responsibility or guilt; your interaction with the material is easily constrained to an intellectual exercise that is kept at a safe distance from personal involvement. Now **that** is entertainment. Ahhh, this feels much more comfortable, and thus more credible. Our ego's job is to make us feel comfortable by redefining and interpreting our perceptions and conclusions to calm our fears and suit our needs. The typical ego can be convincing, cleverly subtle, and is extremely good at its job.

On the other hand, if you do have the energy and drive to find out for yourself, getting the initial kick-off briefing from your Dutch uncle who has been there and done that should greatly reduce the threshold to getting started. The technique is found in Chapter 23, Book 1 – the rest is found in your intent. ◀

Although reading this trilogy demonstrates great effort on your part, digesting it is another matter. Digestion is a much slower, more complex, and more significant process – it determines what you will absorb as opposed to what you will excrete. Being somewhat of an expert in the field of excretion processes, let me offer this advice: While *My Big TOE* is **slowly** digesting, you should take the opportunity to contemplate **your** Big TOE (you have one whether you know it or not); that will make the absorption process as efficient and effective as possible.

The antacid is on the top shelf right next to the extra strength aspirin.

17

■■■

You Must Climb the Mountain to Get a Good View

■■■

There is no such thing as heresy if there is no such thing as belief. Likewise, you cannot be sucked into someone else's belief trap if you do not need a soothing belief. Replacing one belief system with another is of relatively little value. Perhaps there is some value if the new belief system is less limiting than the old one, but the **apparent** lack of limitations won't do you any good if you do not stretch out and take advantage of the new found freedom. A man who will not leave his room because he does not know how, or is afraid to open the door, is trapped just the same whether or not the door is locked.

Now that you have seen the details of the overall model of reality contained within *My Big TOE*, it may be a good idea to re-read the foreword to this trilogy to regain the proper perspective for absorbing and interpreting what you have read. Additionally, look at the last several pages of Chapter 11, Book 2 (begin just after the free will aside) and at the discussion of fractal existence in Chapter 13 of this book. Reading these top-level high altitude summaries will prime you to get the most from the upcoming discussion that integrates *My Big TOE* into traditional Western science and philosophy.

There is a good chance that you will find something there that will help put the Big Picture into a more usable, or at least more comfortable, perspective. Such a review may dramatically facilitate the process of coming to your own conclusions – which is, by the way, your next challenge.

It is always interesting and sometimes informative to take another look from the mountaintop after extensive exploration of the valley. While you are there, you can assess whether or not I made good on the up-front claims that were used to encourage you to buy and read this book when you could have been more comfortable and better entertained watching TV.

If you want to communicate with me directly, go to the My-Big-TOE web page at **http://www.My-Big-TOE.com**. This web address is **not** case sensitive, but **the hyphens are necessary**. You can send email to me and the publisher from this web site, as well as acquire all Big TOE books and other paraphernalia. Here, you can keep up with the latest in Big TOE info, happenings, and discussion groups. By all means, share your complaints, praises, and comments with me by way of the web. It could be fun and educational, help you integrate what you have read, and enable you to be more connected and engaged with others. Best of all, you will find a public place to express your politely worded and erudite opinions, experiences, and learned thoughts – however pro or con they may be. A constructive sharing of ideas, experiences and feelings may go a long way toward helping you develop and grow your own Big TOE. Your experience and insight may present a valuable learning opportunity for me and for others.

You may or may not raise your consciousness and lower your entropy while dancing the Big TOE boogie with kindred spirits at the My-Big-TOE web page, but it might make you feel better to share your feelings and knowledge and vent your angst. You may even bump into an unforeseen opportunity to learn something of value.

My Big TOE is a model that simultaneously makes sense of both your subjective and objective experience as well as defines the ultimate significance of that experience. If you do not bring your experiential data to the table (before, during or after reading this trilogy), you will not get as much as you could from Sections 2 through 5. As long as *MY Big TOE* remains only a pile of words that you can either choose to believe or choose not believe, it cannot effectively serve as a catalyst to your personal growth.

This Big TOE trilogy represents my best effort to facilitate the process of you growing your own big-as-possible TOE based on your personal experience by gently tugging at the constraints that may be limiting your vision. My intent is to set your mind free to find truth, not to pile on another layer of belief on top of what you already have, or replace one of your current beliefs with a new one. Freedom – spiritual, emotional, and intellectual freedom – provides the necessary environment for learning. Open minded skepticism is the primary tool you will need to maintain a free mind capable of significant evolutionary progress.

Don't forget that other models can be different from *My Big TOE* and still be correct within the context of their specific conceptualization. My view is not the only useful or correct view – it is not an exposition of the one truth. If you are looking for the one correct expression of truth, you do not understand the cultural characteristics of expression, or the nature of truth.

A major purpose of this trilogy is to serve as a Big TOE construction kit – a way of looking at reality that helps you make sense of your experience within a larger systems view. Its value lies in its ability to describe all the data from all sources within all cultures in terms of a Western scientific-philosophical context. *My Big TOE* is designed to be most easily comprehended by the Western mind-set; other mind-sets may better understand and get more from other models.

With the *My Big TOE* trilogy, I have made an effort to develop a perspective that loosens up self-imposed constraints while providing a rational structure that will serve as a tower or mountain from which you can leap – soar off on your own – like a Jonathan Livingston Reader.

It is intrinsically difficult to leap and soar from the bottom of the PMR pit where most of us live; a little altitude can be invaluable. With no altitude, we need a long running start, which is much more difficult to achieve and often leaves us flapping furiously yet not getting off the ground.

Grounded! Caught in a belief trap, flapping about pathetically, unable to take flight into the reality that lies within. Can you relate to this pathetic bird-rat-being-pit-dweller-person?

You must climb the mountain to get a good view. You must look for the conceptual high ground from which to launch your vision of a personal Big TOE. At least, you must be able to differentiate up from down; if you can do that, and persevere in your effort, the rest will follow.

One note of caution. There are those who would entice you to get into their psychotropic drug cannon. They will offer to launch you into inner space like Bozo, the Human Cannonball Clown at the circus. **Do not take the trip**! If you do, you will no doubt end up a clown like Bozo except there will be no net and no applause. Consciousness altering drugs do **not** constitute a viable path to an increased quality of consciousness and are a thousand times more likely to be a serious problem than a serious solution.

If you cannot fly on your own, being shot out of a cannon to imitate flight constitutes a short irrelevant trip to nowhere ... and then ... SPLAT!

Being shot up into inner-space like a Fourth of July bottle rocket cannot teach you anything at all about flying, navigating, interpreting, or effectively utilizing thought-space; the view is short-lived and the trip can be deadly to your spiritual progress. In fact, using a chemical rocket to provide access to inner space almost always makes learning to grow and soar on your own more difficult.

It is said that misery loves company. Do not join the losers who are looking for a shortcut or a good time. Traveling down the path of chemically induced altered states of consciousness eventually and surely will take you to the opposite of both.

Because we live in an environment that is constantly trying to sell, manipulate and control, we are conditioned to defend our ego's constructs and to argue with and resist what others are constantly throwing at us. Eventually, by force of habit, this conditioned response hears me say – "I know more about these things than you ever will, simply believe what I tell you until you can figure it out for yourself" – despite what I have said to the contrary. Do you ever feel as though you are living in a grade-B reality where the zombies have taken over the world?

I have some good news and some bad news. The good news is that absolutely nobody but you can block your path toward quality consciousness. The bad news is that absolutely nobody but you can unblock your path toward quality consciousness. Actually, the bad news is not that bad. It simply means there are some things that money, status, good looks, sex appeal, and political power cannot buy – some things you either have to do for yourself or do without. Opportunity is everywhere; it is only gumption and vision that are in short supply.

18

■■■

The Significance of Insignificance

■■■

If improving the quality of your consciousness seems to be the point of existence, does that imply that worldly (PMR) pursuits, such as studying mathematics, physics, philosophy, basket weaving, digging ditches, or becoming an artist, are a waste of time? Absolutely not! You should do something besides contemplate your Big TOE. Everyone should have something externally productive to do with his or her time – something that is at least of some value to others. It is not what you do that is important – nor is it how valuable it is to others that is important: It is what you learn in the process of doing it that is important. For this reason, almost any job or activity will suffice because it is your interaction with yourself and others that creates many of the best learning opportunities.

If, after reading *My Big TOE*, everything in PMR seems less interesting and less significant, you have missed an important point. It is the experience we have in PMR that gives us the opportunity to learn by making choices that are precipitated by interaction with others. All sorts of activity in PMR – butcher, baker, candlestick maker, doctor, lawyer, Indian chief, housewife, teacher, physicist, bum, executive, or guru – all provide the opportunity you need to learn and grow the quality of your consciousness.

It is not that any profession or life's work has become less important because you now have a bigger picture. With a bigger picture there are other things that are also important that did not exist in the previous little picture. Physical possessions, family, friends, or your career, for example, are not any more or less a part of your life than they were before you grasped the Big Picture; it is you who may change the way you value them as your ego, knowledge, wisdom, or perspective changes. From a new larger perspective, as the ego value of what you do subsides, the real value (interactions with yourself, your tasks, and with other people) grows. Your career, or whatever you do, may seem less important in the Big Picture, but the potential value its interactions have for you should seem more important from your larger view.

What you are interested in is a function of what turns you on, and where you invest your energy. Again, a bigger view adds additional interesting things into the mix of possible things in which you can invest your energy. As you evolve your being (grow the quality and lower the entropy of your consciousness), the focus of your energy investment constantly shifts because a broadened reality includes new awareness that changes the potential investment mix.

Simply look at your life – say from age five to your current age – to see the truth of that statement. As you have grown up, the things that are important to you constantly change as your awareness broadens. The process of changing your investment focus continues as long as you continue to grow. If you are able, interested, and willing, the rate of growth accelerates after thirty-five – the growth rate curve can continue to be exponential for some time, and does not peter-out and go asymptotic (to the time axis) as most people think (imagine a plot of growth rate versus time). Your growth rate becomes asymptotic (slows to a crawl) only when you believe you know almost everything important.

That sense of knowing it all, (at least everything significant) usually blossoms at two, then again during the teenage years, and then gels, or becomes permanent, for most people around the age of forty. At two it is called "terrible," during the teen years it is called "self absorbed" and "wild"; at forty it is called "mature" (obviously it is the older group that makes up the names). Knowing almost everything important is seen as the end point of growing up. This is like a sheltered (doesn't get out much) four-ounce juice glass half full of prune juice thinking it contains all the fluid on the planet. It knows nothing of the world's great lakes, oceans, rivers and seas, and being secure in its ignorance, feels self-important and complete in its mastery of fluids. Oh my! Poor little delusional juice glass!

If *My Big TOE* leaves you feeling deflated, it is because you are seeing the juice glass as being half empty instead of half full. Where you are now, what you are presently doing is almost certainly a great place from which to learn and grow. You do not need to make changes to your environment; you need only to make changes to yourself.

If you continue to feel deflated because you are not making sufficient progress in changing yourself, because you do not know how to start, cheer up – it's easier than you think. Not starting because you do not know how is like a one-year-old baby believing it will never walk or talk because it does not know how. Bullpucky! That is a copout attitude laying down a defeatist rap. Try this rap instead:

Just go do it!

Do it now!

That is all there is to it.

Wow!

Just go do it

You don't need to know how!

If you can sing that to a funky beat while you play the imaginary bongos on a tabletop you are on your way! Go! Go! Amigo!

What? You do not want to look nuts in front of your friends? I understand, you are new at this sort of thing – tell your friends that this mind-rap is actually a secret Tibetan chant recently translated from a primitive Sanskrit text found etched at the bottom of an ancient "Monks Do It Better" bumper sticker. Also remember, actual sanity flows from freedom while only pretend sanity flows from conformity.

Additionally, you might want to work on the following: Begin to understand your beliefs and their limitations. Inspect your ego regularly to see if it is growing or shrinking and expose some of its more blatant fantasies to yourself, then to your loved ones, and finally to your friends. Dedicate some of your energy every day to finding and verifying the truth. Become aware of your motivations and intents. Turn off the TV and get acquainted with your mind. Learn to meditate (see Chapter 23, Book 1). Be kind and loving in all your interactions with others. Stop thinking about yourself and your wants, needs, and desires. Figure out what your fears are and outgrow them. And above all, continue to objectively taste that pudding to see how you are doing. Only real measurable, bona fide objective results are acceptable. If you do not get results that you, as well as others, can easily see after a serious six-month effort, do something else. Be patient, real progress takes serious dedication over a long time. Have fun always.

Just go do it. You don't need to know how!

19

■■■

Traveling in Good Company

■■■

Since Big Truth is the same for everyone for all time, I figured that there
must be lots of other similar material published somewhere. After I
completed Chapter 18 of Book 3, I decided it was time to do a literature
search and find out what science and philosophy had to say about Big
Truth. I know, I was supposed to do that first – however, *My Big TOE* is
not meant to be a scholarly work that merely adds an original twist to the
work of others. This Big TOE is between you and me, dear reader: Its
value to you defines its significance to me and what anybody else thinks
about it is not relevant. My goal is to point out and explain the logical pattern that I have noticed in my own experience. Since I am not trying to
convince you of its correctness, I don't need much help. After all, it is the
results of my experience that I am writing about and it is the results of
your experience that judges the value of my effort. If you and I are not
the world's top experts on the meaning and significance of our personal
experience, who is?

What I found out in my search – restricted to the processes of science,
mathematics and logic – was that the ideas presented in *My Big TOE* are
ideas that many individuals, judged by history to be great thinkers, have
touched on. Even if many of these stellar individuals did not have the
entire picture, they often saw a significant part of it.

I am not, I must confess, a particularly widely read individual. The
upside is that what I have written in *My Big TOE* is uniquely mine and has
not been influenced very much by others. This is no intellectually slick
term paper laced with expert references and quotes to prove the point;
there is no point to prove. Fortunately, the truth is the same for everybody, and all seekers who find any particular Big Truth will more or less

reach the same conclusions. I expect that there are hundreds of books that share many of the concepts laid out in *My Big TOE*. No one has the market cornered on truth. Wisdom (both pseudo and real) has found creative outlets throughout the ages and will continue to do so.

On the other hand, the down side is that I cannot very easily come up with intellectually satisfying, cool-sounding quotes from big intellectual guns that if sprinkled throughout my text would lend credibility to my discourse (particularly at chapter headings, as is the current fashion). I have often thought that when the quotes are actually relevant, this can be a clever and effective literary device.

Not being that clever, I am forced to find other ways to invoke the knowledge of others and thus give the reader the illusion that there is indeed safety in numbers – that thinking big ideas that lie off the beaten path is not such a dangerous and crazy thing to do.

The only real danger is that once you find new knowledge, you automatically gain the responsibility for that knowledge. With both new knowledge and new responsibility, your growth rate will begin to accelerate dramatically. Before long you are a changed person! This, without a doubt, is the main danger associated with traveling the Path of Knowledge: that you might grow up as the quality of your consciousness improves. That may not sound too bad, but if those around you do not share your new broadened perspective, traveling through inner-space can be a lonely trip. Of course, you and Peter Pan can avoid that result if you want to.

The scientific literature is full of material that supports many of the concepts in *My Big TOE*. From physicists of the caliber of Albert Einstein and David Bohm we find several quotes that clearly show their sense of the larger reality.

> *"I wished to show that space-time is not necessarily something to which one can ascribe a separate existence, independently of the actual objects of physical reality. Physical objects are not in space, but these objects are spatially extended. In this way the concept of 'empty space' loses its meaning."*
> — ALBERT EINSTEIN JUNE 9TH, 1952 NOTE
> TO THE FIFTEENTH EDITION OF *RELATIVITY*

Here Dr. Einstein is trying to explain that space-time is not something that physical objects exist within. He thought that space and physical objects were of the same substance – all were part of a single unified field. What appear to be solid objects are merely regions of higher field density than what appears to be empty space. What you perceive as reality is merely your experience of the various interactions within the unified field. The bottom line, according to Einstein, is that there is no such thing as physical space. Physical space (what you think you live in – what you **believe** constitutes your reality) is merely an illusion. Without physical space, there can be no physical reality. Einstein's deepest and most intuitive understanding of reality was expressed by his effort to develop a **nonphysical** TOE that he called "Unified Field Theory."

> *"If we think of the field as being removed, there is no 'space' which remains, since space does not have an independent existence."*
> —ALBERT EINSTEIN, *GENERALIZATION OF GRAVITATION THEORY*

> *"Reality is merely an illusion, albeit a very persistent one."*
> — ALBERT EINSTEIN

The following quote, attributed to "one of Einstein's letters" by Rudolf v. B. Rucker in his book *Geometry, Relativity And The Fourth Dimension* (p. 118) and also found in *Quantum Reality, Beyond the New Physics*, p. 250, captures Einstein's larger sense of reality and purpose.

> *"A human being is part of the whole, called by us 'Universe,' a part limited in time and space. He experiences himself, his thought and feeling, as something separated from the rest – a kind of optical delusion of his consciousness. This delusion is a kind of prison for us, restricting us to our personal desires and to affection for a few persons nearest to us. Our task must be to free ourselves from this prison by widening our circle of compassion to embrace all living creatures and the whole nature in this beauty. Nobody is able to achieve this completely, but the striving for such achievement is in itself a part of the liberation and a foundation of inner security."*
> — ALBERT EINSTEIN

It is clear from Einstein's many writings that space-time is not the place where we live, but rather a field of which we are a part. Mass (including our bodies) is merely a higher density portion of that pervasive field – matter bumps on the lumps in the space-time consciousness sheet. That this fundamental field was nonphysical and associated with consciousness was not as clear to Einstein as it was to his friend, associate, and fellow physicist, David Bohm.

*"To meet the challenge before us our notions of cosmology and of
the general nature of reality must have room in them to permit
a consistent account of consciousness. Vice versa, our notions of
consciousness must have room in them to understand what it means
for its content to be 'reality as a whole.' The two sets of notions
together should then be such as to allow for an understanding
as to how consciousness and reality are related."*
— DAVID BOHM FROM THE INTRODUCTION TO
WHOLENESS AND THE IMPLICATE ORDER

From Max Jammer's book *The Concepts of Space* with an enthusiastic forward and endorsement by Albert Einstein, we have further clarification (p. 171):
*"Hence it is clear that the space of physics is not, in the last analysis,
anything given in nature or independent of human thought.
It is a function of our conceptual scheme [mind]. Space as conceived
by Newton proved to be an illusion, although for practical purposes
a very fruitful illusion – indeed so fruitful that the concepts of
absolute space and absolute time will forever remain in the
background of our daily experience."*
From the same source (p. 175) we find the great mathematician and physicist Karl Friedrich Gauss *"considered the three dimensionality of space not to be an inherent quality of space, but as a specific peculiarity of the human soul [consciousness]."* Also we find out from Dr. Jammer that time is the fundamental quantity and that space is a derivative of time (p. 169). Dr. Jammer says, *"This fact is of extraordinary significance because it proves that space measurements are reducible to time measurements. Time is therefore logically prior to space."*

I am sure a high-frequency state-changing spaceless nonphysical consciousness like AUO was very happy to get that news. If you are trying to remember where we first derived that conclusion, look in Chapter 31 of Book 1.

Eugene P. Vigner, a Nobel Prize winner and one of the leading physicists of the twentieth century, wrote a paper entitled: *The Place of Consciousness in Modern Physics* wherein he discuses the future of quantum physics. Dr. Vigner said: *"It will remain remarkable, in what ever way our future concepts may develop, that the very study of the external world led to the **scientific** conclusion that the content of the consciousness is the ultimate universal reality."*

Unfortunately, the non-objective (from the view of PMR) process that is required to access the science of consciousness ("the ultimate universal reality") was not fully appreciated. It may seems obvious to you that consciousness belongs to the individual and therefore is personal and cannot be studied in the same manner as a moon-rock, but at the time, and even today, this is not clear to everyone. However, the objective scientific importance of subjective experience was not overlooked entirely.

Willis W Harmon (Ph.D.), noted futurist, forward thinker, Director of the US Educational Policy Research Center at Stanford University, in a 1969 paper entitled *The New Copernican Revolution* discusses the coming science of subjective experience.

"The science of man's subjective experience is in its infancy.
Even so, some of its foreshadowings are evident. With the classification
of these questions into the realm of empirical inquiry, we can
anticipate an acceleration of research in this area.
"Young and incomplete as the science of subjective experience is, it
nevertheless already contains what may very well be extremely
significant precursors of tomorrow's image of man's potentialities."

At this point Dr. Harmon provides a discussion of what he terms "...an impressive amount of substantiating evidence." Next he describes the ongoing research that supports his projection. He then goes on to say:

"Assuming that the evidence substantiating these propositions continues to
mount, they have the most profound implications for the future. For they
say most powerfully that we have undersold man, underestimated his pos-
sibilities, and misunderstood what is needed for what Boulding terms 'the
great transition.' They imply that the most profound revolution of the edu-
cational system would not be the cybernation of knowledge transmission,
but the infusion of an exalted image of what man can be and the cultiva-
tion of an enhanced self-image in each individual child.
"It is perhaps not too early to predict some of the characteristics of the new
science. Preliminary indications suggest at least the following:
"Although we have been speaking of it as a science of subjective
experience, one of its dominant characteristics will be a realizing of the
subjective-objective dichotomy. The range between perceptions shared by all
or practically all, and those which are unique to one individual, will be
assumed to be much more of a continuum than a sharp division between
'the world out there' and what goes on 'in my head.'

*"Related to this will be the incorporation, in some form, of the age-old
yet radical doctrine that we perceive the world and ourselves in it
as we have been culturally 'hypnotized' to perceive it. The typical
commonsense-scientific view of reality will be considered to be a valid
but partial view – a particular metaphor, so to speak. Others, such as
certain religious or metaphysical views, will be considered ... equally
valid but more appropriate for certain areas of human experience.*

*"The new science will incorporate some ways of referring to the
subjective experiencing of a unity in all things (the 'more' of William
James, the 'All' of Bugental, the 'Divine Ground' of Aldous Huxley's
The Perennial Philosophy).*

*"It will include some sort of mapping or ordering of states of
consciousness transcending the usual conscious awareness (Bucke's
'Cosmic Consciousness,' the 'enlightenment' of Zen, and similar concepts).*

*"It will take account of the subjective experiencing of a 'higher self'
and will view favorably the development of a self-image congruent with
this experience (Bugental's 'I-process,' Emerson's 'Over-soul,' Assagioli's
'True Self,' Brunton's 'Over-self,' the Atman of Vendanta, and so on).*

*"It will allow for a much more unified view of human experiences
now categorized under such diverse headings as creativity, hypnosis,
mystical experience, psychedelic drugs, extra-sensory perception,
psychokinesis, and related phenomena.*

*"It will include a much more unified view of the processes of
personal change and emergence which take place within the
contexts of psychotherapy, education (in the sense of 'know thyself'),
and religion (as spiritual growth)."*

Dr. Harmon's vision and understanding of the fundamental scientific
and individual importance of individuated (subjective) consciousness was
right on the money but considerably more ahead of his time than he sus-
pected. Never underestimate the power of the visionless center of objective science to maintain the conceptual status quo. Why did the vast
majority of Western thinkers believe the earth to be flat when it had been
demonstrated and logically confirmed to be spherical by several well-
known and well-respected scientist-philosophers hundreds of years earlier? The political correctness of scientific **belief** weighs heavily at the center. Sometimes brilliance at the conceptual edge must be patient before
the less flexible conceptual center is capable of seeing the light.

Let's return to the discipline of physics to see the next piece of the reality puzzle fall into place. Albert Einstein (Unified Field Theory) asserted

a nonphysical field as the basis for both matter specifically and reality in general, thereby moving science closer to the truth, but he did not appreciate the discrete digital nature of both space and time or the role of consciousness (instead of space-time) as the primary energy field. Einstein's student and colleague, the great quantum physicist David Bohm (along with a few of the best Quantum Mechanics theorists such as Niels Bohr, Werner Heisenberg, and Eugene Vigner) made the consciousness connection but missed the digital connection and the Big Picture.

"One has to find a possibility to avoid the continuum (together with space and time) altogether. But I have not the slightest idea what kind of elementary concepts could be used in such a theory."
— LETTER FROM ALBERT EINSTEIN
TO DAVID BOHM OCTOBER 28, 1954

Physicist Dr. Edward Fredkin of MIT, Boston University, and Carnegie Mellon finally made the digital connection. In 1992 Dr. Fredkin published two papers: *A New Cosmogony* and *Finite Nature*. In these formal scientific papers, presented within traditional scientific forums, Dr. Fredkin developed rationale supporting both quantized space and quantized time, along with a description of reality as fundamentally digital. The science of information theory and mathematics lead him to postulate an "Ultimate Computer" as the basis of a digital reality that computes our physical existence.

"If space and time and matter and energy are all a consequence of the informational processes running on the Ultimate Computer then everything in our universe is represented by that informational process. The place where the computer is, the engine that runs that process, we choose to call 'Other'.
"Where did Other come from? This question is actually quite easy to fence with. The nature of systems of laws that can support computation is very much broader than the nature of systems that are limited to the physics of our universe. In other words, many of the properties of our world that are necessary for our world to take the form it has are not necessary for other kinds of worlds that can support universal computation. Universal computation, the kind that can simulate other general-purpose computers, is even a property of all ordinary commercial computers.
"There is no need for a space with three dimensions; computation can do just fine in spaces of any number of dimensions! The space does not have to be locally connected like our world is. Computation does not require

conservation laws or symmetries. A world that supports computation does not have to have time as we know it, there is no need for beginnings and endings. Computation is compatible within worlds where something can come from nothing, where resources are finite, infinite or variable."

Dr. Fredkin goes on to prove that "other" must be other than physical, that is, nonphysical from the PMR point of view. It would appear that Dr. Fredkin is talking about TBC and the space-time rule-set; yet Dr. Fredkin's work is wholly rooted in modern math, information theory, and contemporary physics.

Dr. Fredkin continues to analyze ("intelligent speculation" as he puts it) the beginnings of our universe.

"If we assume that the Ultimate Computer was purposefully constructed in 'Other,' we can immediately answer the puzzle of the origin of the Universe. It's simply a matter of the following process taking place in 'Other.' The initial conditions are set into the engine and the engine is set into motion; it starts to compute. Those two steps are outside the domain of physics."

That passage from *A New Cosmogony* should remind you of our description of The Big Digital Bang – The Big Simulation – discussed in Chapter 29 of Book 2, and in Chapters 1 and 9 of Book 3. Dr. Fredkin continues to explore the nature of "other":

"As to the question 'Why didn't the thing in Other just do it in its head?' The answer is quite straightforward: Doing it on a computer is exactly the same thing as doing it in one's head [with consciousness]. Both are examples of using an informational process to get to the answer.
We are not referring to the thing in Other finding an analytical solution in its head (the speedup theorem forbids such solutions) but rather to it imagining each step of some cellular automaton in its head. Strangely enough, that's exactly the same as doing it on a computer."

Is it not obvious that digital consciousness simulating OS nicely fits the form, function and nature of Fredkin's "other"? What Dr. Fredkin did not understand was that consciousness **is** the computer. I find it interesting that information theory, physics, and mathematics, once again (this time from an entirely different starting position) point to consciousness as the ultimate reality, the fundamental source of All That Is.

Dr. Fredkin seems to have started something with his concept of a calculating (simulating) digital reality based in a nonphysical computer. Today there are a growing number of physicists, computer and information scientists, and mathematicians scattered around the world that pursue research in what has come to be called digital physics. Digital physics, like relativity and quantum mechanics, is serious hard-core science that is, for the majority of people, still way out on the edge.

▶ Let's pause a moment to collect together what some of the most respected scientists of our time have thus far jointly discovered. 1) What we perceive as our local physical reality is actually a nonphysical virtual reality, a subset of a larger more fundamental reality. 2) The doorway to experiencing this larger reality is through the individual's subjective mind. 3) The larger reality is based upon consciousness, which is the basic substance, energy, or media of existence. 4) The larger reality is discrete and must be the result of digital computation: The consciousness of (3) above is a digital consciousness and that the virtual reality of (1) above is a digital simulation.

Ladies and gentlemen, are you astounded to find out that *My Big TOE* has explained, derived, and pulled together, within a coherent theoretical framework, some of the best theoretical efforts of contemporary modern science?

Jeez, I don't know about you, but it astounded the hell out of me!

Notice how the seemingly wild-eyed conjecture of one old Dutch Uncle-dude, turns out to derive results that are very similar to the results derived by some of the twentieth century's most respected and innovative scientists.

This trilogy represents serious science folks – the bridge between physics and metaphysics, mind and matter, normal and paranormal. It delivers the first look at a Unified Theory Of Everything – not the way traditional science expected it, but then, if it was the way traditional science expected it, it couldn't actually be a **Big** TOE could it? If you want to see the unified Big Picture, you have to step out of the box that limits your understanding and knowledge. You cannot see it from the vantage point of the old paradigms.

As advertised, *My Big TOE* delivers the integrated results of contemporary modern physics to your doorstep. Why are you so surprised? Did you think *My Big TOE* is not a serious scientific effort? Why not? When you formulate answers to those last two questions, be sure to inspect them for hidden belief traps. A typically trapped mind tends to **believe** that all that goofy metaphysical AUM-stuff necessarily moves the reality model of *My Big TOE* out of the realm of objective science and into the realm of non-provable conjecture. Such a mind **believes** that if AUM is not the **result** of a physical measurement or logically definable by an equation, then AUM falls outside the scope of science.

By now, dear reader, you should immediately recognize the illogic of that particular belief trap. Remember that the logic of the little virtual reality applies only within that little virtual reality. (You may want to re-look at the logic of beginnings discussion in Book 1, Chapter 18.) A virtual reality is, by definition, a closed logical system – its physics is merely a symbolic (mathematical) representation of that logic. The logical causality of the Big Picture cannot be derived from the logical causality of the little picture. The Big Picture cannot logically be contained within, or be a subset of, the little picture. You cannot arrive at the Big Picture if you never leave the little picture.

Einstein and the great quantum theorists got stuck because they were trying to derive the larger reality in terms of the logic (mathematics) of the smaller reality. Little picture logic (the mathematical physics of the space-time rule-set) can tell you only about the little picture. These scientists bumped into the little picture to Big Picture boundary, but could not penetrate that boundary with little picture logic alone. The Big Picture appears to be logically impossible, and thus becomes invisible, when viewed through little picture paradigms.

That *My Big TOE* is presented as a **non-mathematical** extension of the limited science of our virtual physical reality is a logical **requirement**, not a scientific weakness. The logical causality of the Big Picture can be expressed in terms of its own symbolic logic (mathematics), but such constructions are of limited use in thought-space. Before the scientific and mathematical types get lost here, consider the evolutionary purpose of a consciousness system.

Physicists still have a lot to learn about the space-time rule-set that defines our little picture virtual physical reality. Because that rule-set defines a digital virtual simulation within a larger digital reality, little TOEs may need to embrace some of the digital magic we have found so entertaining at the movies and so useful on our desktops. Even so, little picture science and applied mathematics (little picture logic) can never lead directly to a Big TOE. To get there, to experience the Big Picture, you must leave the little picture behind and step through the portal of your subjective (from the little picture view) mind into the larger reality of digital consciousness.

Consider what the little picture scientific establishment will tell you: An AUM-digital-consciousness-system-thing could not possibly be the **larger and more fundamental** reality because it is not **exclusively** manifested as a **physical** substance in the little **virtual** physical reality. Can you imagine a more illogical and irrational belief? You would think that this belief is incredibly stupid if you were not raised to accept that it is unquestionably true.

It should be clear that consciousness is both nonphysical and real – that it is primarily a personal thing and therefore subjective. Furthermore, to separate the external from the internal, the real from the imagined, you should insist on testing and confirming the operational realness and significance of subjective experience by demanding measurable, repeatable, **objective** results before assessing the value of that experience.

We could go on and on exposing this particular PMR *über alles* trap, but we have covered that ground in great detail already. Those who get it do not need to hear it again, and those who do not get it need to wait until they are more open and ready – until they can look beyond the old paradigms and belief systems that have captured and imprisoned their mind. If you are not sure whether you get it or not, finish all three books of the trilogy, give it a rest for a month or so, and then read it again starting with Section 2. Because of *My Big TOE*'s unusualness, and because it is nearly impossible **not** to accept the core beliefs of your culture, it is extremely difficult to get it all the first time through. I know how disconcerting and annoying that thought must be; nonetheless, it is a true statement that applies to most of us.

The wasted potential of a self-limited mind is a sad happening in any reality. A larger consciousness system appears as unsupported conjecture only to those who will not take the time or make the effort to explore (experience) and assess the Big Picture scientifically. Just a little open-minded research and experimentation is all that is required to lend credence to the existence of the larger consciousness system of which we are a part.

Oh good grief! Do you hear all that hysterical shrieking and banging about? That's the sound of the defenders of the scientific and cultural status quo and sacred belief systems building walls instead of bridges. Not to worry, all the folks quoted in this chapter have heard that sound many times before. As always, if the data support it, raise it up, use it, experiment with it, seek new understanding; if it does not, let it self-destruct under the weight of its own failure to produce a greater, more productive paradigm. Fortunately, the truth is not delicate; it can stand up to whatever comes, for however long it takes.

Here, an objective group-proof organized by the establishment (con) or the anti-establishment (pro) has no merit. It is up to you, dear reader, to develop your own proof (knowledge) through your own experience. Let no one succeed in providing the answers for you. At the core, you are consciousness: you have access to all the answers – go find them for yourself and they will make you whole.◀

▶▶ Following the herd, no matter which way it is going, inevitably leads to stasis and dysfunction. Following the herd or conceptual center, allows you to trade the **opportunity** for personal progress and growth for an easy and safe no-brainer glide through existence. Unfortunately, procrastination and immediate gratification team up to produce the worst possible long-term strategy for consciousness evolution.

The herd appears to validate each member with its mutual support mantra of "I'm OK, you're OK, we are all OK as long as we stick together." Fear and ego provide the herd's cohesive forces. Your individual consciousness is a personal thing, not a group thing. If you have the courage to break loose from the herd, don't worry; the larger world is not nearly as scary as it looks. Gather strength and resolve from the fact that, as a solitary seeker, you are following the path of all innovators, discoverers, and creators. Only as an individual do you have the potential to make a significant difference where it counts the most.◀◀

▶ It seems that we have accomplished a great deal with the two basic assumptions (consciousness and evolution) that we started with in Chapter 24 of Book 1. Neither assumption should appear that unusual because we experience a **profound** and **immeasurable** (nonphysical) personal consciousness every day of our lives, and because we have been observing evolution at work in the little picture for a long time. From those simple assumptions we have derived a model of reality, a Big TOE that encompasses all previous knowledge as well as derives new knowledge from a less limiting, more general reality paradigm. Our consciousness is our personal connection to that larger reality – our ticket to view and experience the Big Picture.

Guess what, dear reader? You have successfully been doing Big TOE physics throughout the last four sections of this trilogy. You have, relatively easily and quickly, derived from basic principles the same results that Einstein, Bohm, Bohr, Vigner, Harmon, Fredkin, and other top scientists took several decades and tons of complex mathematical analysis to reach. Furthermore, you have pulled together all of their various pieces of cleverness, discovery, and intuition into one unified whole, something many have tried to accomplish. However, until now, no one had been able to find the perspective wherein they could glimpse the entire Big Picture – a perspective where all the pieces integrate nicely into one. You have now accomplished this long-sought and scientifically remarkable feat. I am very proud of you. I will wait here while you go tell your mother.◀

In the Big Picture, science and philosophy once again become one – two aspects of the same knowledge. We have heard from the scientists; now let's hear what the philosophers have been saying. I will mention only a few of the West's most famous philosophers, all from the group called modern philosophers that arrive at their conclusions through rigorous inductive and deductive reasoning. This is not the king of the opinion hill philosophy that dominated before Descartes, but rather an intensely rational system of logic more closely related to mathematics than persuasive discourse. (Note: Many of the history of philosophy factoids briefly and superficially scattered over the next few pages were cut and pasted directly from Microsoft's Encarta Encyclopedia; how I pitch them is all my own. If you think my history of philosophy facts are not precisely the way you remember them, don't bug me – go see Bill.)

The most famous of all the mutterings of all the philosophers is attributable to Rene Descartes, the initiator of modern philosophy: *"I think, therefore I am."* This simple phrase is a tribute to the primacy of consciousness as a core contributor to any fundamental conception of reality.

Eighteenth-century German philosopher Immanuel Kant held that all that can be known of things in themselves is the way in which they appear in experience – there is no way of knowing what they are substantially in themselves. He also held that the fundamental principles of all science are essentially grounded in the constitution of the mind rather than being derived from the external world. Does this remind you of our discussion of experience in Chapter 32 of Book 2 where we separated the experienceable reality from the un-experienceable reality that lies beyond our limited physical perception?

Gottfried Wilhelm Leibniz was considered a universal genius by his contemporaries and by history. He made brilliant original contributions not only to mathematics and philosophy, but also to theology, law, diplomacy, politics, history, philology, and physics. In the philosophy expounded by Leibniz, the universe is composed of countless conscious centers of spiritual force or energy, known as monads. Each monad represents an individual microcosm, mirroring the universe in varying degrees of perfection and developing independently of all other monads. The universe that these monads constitute is the harmonious result of a divine plan. Do you make the connection between Leibniz's monads and the fundamental dynamic pattern of all existence and creation that forms the basis of the consciousness-evolution fractal we discussed in Chapter 13 of book 3?

Johann Gottlieb Fichte transformed Kant's critical idealism into absolute idealism by eliminating Kant's things in themselves and making the will the ultimate reality. Fichte maintained that the world is created by an absolute ego, of which the human will is a partial manifestation and which tends toward God-consciousness as an unrealized ideal.

Friedrich Wilhelm Joseph von Schelling went still further in reducing all things to the self-realizing activity of an absolute spirit (individuated unit of consciousness), which he identified with the creative impulse in nature.

One of the most influential philosophical minds of the 19th century was the German philosopher George Wilhelm Friedrich Hegel, whose system of absolute idealism was based on a conception of logic in which conflict and contradiction are regarded as necessary elements of truth, and truth is regarded as a process rather than a fixed state of things. The source of all reality, for Hegel, is an absolute spirit, or cosmic reason, which develops from abstract, undifferentiated being.

The Danish philosopher Søren Kierkegaard attacked the concept that objective reason is the only source of truth. His eloquent defense of feeling and of a subjective approach to the problems of life became one of the main sources of 20th-century existential philosophy.

As you see, modern analytical (logic based, not belief-based) philosophers have been hot on the heels of a larger more primary reality that is based upon mind, consciousness, or spirit. They have been much closer to Big Truth for centuries than the scientists but didn't know how to integrate their knowledge with the physical world. These philosophers did not fully appreciate the subjective component of reality, or that subjective information requires an objective assessment (tasting the pudding) before its value can be determined.

Without these understandings it was difficult for philosophers, and even more difficult for their followers, to differentiate knowledge from pseudo-knowledge. In an age mesmerized by the results of objective science, narrowly focused critics had little trouble discounting the significance of philosophy's contribution toward understanding a reality defined entirely by physical measurement.

Western philosophers eventually succumbed to both their critics and their culture. They restricted their explorations of reality to remain within the rational boundaries set by the limited understanding of little picture objective causality. They immediately fell from the top of the intellectual relevancy heap (where the title Doctor of Philosophy was the highest of intellectual honors) to the bottom of the heap where philosophers are seen as impractical academicians engaged in mind games that are more or less irrelevant to the real world. Philosophy, when focused on the Big Picture that lies beyond cultural belief traps, can be as potent a tool for discovering Big Truth as science. When it comes to ferreting out Big Truth, neither tool works very well by itself; dramatic success can only occur when science and philosophy work together.

Many philosophers understand the synergy of this connectedness on an intuitive level and carefully track the philosophical implications of science. However, they remain frustrated at being unable to contribute very much to a greater unified understanding of the whole. Today, science leads the search for truth while philosophy provides ad hoc commentary in the margins.

Most scientists think philosophy is a waste of time; fortunately, the best scientists do not share that view. They work with their intuition as well as their high-tech tools and have a larger sense of how their work fits into the whole. Defining that whole is seen to fall within the purview of philosophy. Scientists, the caliber of Albert Einstein (as well as the others mentioned above), realize that science and philosophy are two sides of the same coin, and that one-day, when we fully understand the reality of which we are a part, science and philosophy must coalesce into one unified understanding.

By definition, conceptual breakthroughs must necessarily be found outside the boundaries of what is commonly accepted. A profound understanding of reality, a coming together of science and philosophy, can occur only within the Big Picture. When our understanding is complete and whole, all the puzzle pieces fit nicely together. As long as our understanding remains fragmented by our limiting beliefs, competing culturally correct cliques within the little picture will define and therefore limit our vision of reality. The breakthrough solutions that both the scientists and philosophers have been seeking for many decades lie outside the little picture; one cannot get to them without stepping beyond the limits of PMR.

When scientific paradigms (such as the universality of objective causality) become sacred and unquestionable, breakthroughs become impossible. What appears as a weakness in the credibility and scientific stature of *My Big TOE* from the view of the old PMR *über alles* paradigms turns out to be a necessary logical requirement and a condition of credibility from a more expansive, less limited viewpoint.

Appreciating that the dichotomy of modern science and philosophy is an artifact of Big Picture ignorance expressing a limited view will help the reader put *My Big TOE* into a more integrated and unified perspective. To this end, let's round up the concepts we have tossed about in the last several pages and summarize their significance to the bottom line of *My Big TOE*.

As matter and mind split into what appeared to be disconnected opposites, science and philosophy became estranged. Neither could say anything important about the other. Now that *My Big TOE* has shown the mind-matter dichotomy to be a perceptual delusion – all is consciousness – science and philosophy may once again unite as complementary approaches to the same truth. **Good science is good because of the quality of its methodology, rational process, and logic – period**. To further restrict it to a limited little picture causality or local PMR logic is to shut it off from the possibility of explaining its beginnings or seeing the bigger picture.

Scientists require experimentation (a careful objective examination of reality) to separate fact from hypotheses. Within the subjective science of Dr. Harmon, **you** must personally plan and execute your own experiments and derive your own conclusions. Group-proofs, peer review, and majority rule are irrelevant within the mind-space of your personal consciousness. Careful processes and **objective** pudding tasting must be employed before personal science can discover Big Truth.

Similarly, **good philosophy is good because of the quality of its methodology, rational process, and logic – period.** The gap between philosophy and science is not as wide as you might think; one tends more to the possibilities, the other to the actualities. When we explore our reality from a Big Picture perspective, these two approaches to truth become complementary and mutually supportive. It is only when we are far from Big Truth, when we are out of balance – obsessed with the details of an apparently objective physical reality to the exclusion of all else – that science and philosophy seem to exist at opposite poles. It is our inability to see and understand the Big Picture, our lack of inner balance, and our limited PMR paradigms that drive an imaginary wedge between science and philosophy, between mind and matter, between normal and paranormal. The idea that science produces facts while philosophy produces arguments is a simple delusion born of a common prejudice and small view.

Here is an interesting historical comment on the subject. Is not a Ph.D. in Physics, or anything else, a doctor (D) of Philosophy (Ph)? It certainly appears that a long time ago we were less confused on this particular issue than we are now. The scientific attitude that PMR and its little picture logic represent the only possible reality is a common cultural belief that has tricked us into discarding some of the wisdom we had previously acquired. On the other hand, it helped jettison a ton of useless baggage that was holding us back. Obviously, the science-philosophy, mind-matter, normal-paranormal split represented an evolutionary process we sorely needed to go through.

Having made it through our superstitious phase, perhaps now we have grown up enough to simultaneously see a bigger picture and demand objective clarity. Perhaps over the last few hundred years we have learned more than all the kings horses and all the kings men and will be able to put the Big Picture back together again – this time with all the advantages (science and technology) and none of the drawbacks (superstition and belief). That's progress ladies and gentlemen: science eventually saving itself (and everything else) from the ravages of science. No, we are not out of the dark yet, but *My Big TOE* should shed enough light to enable many individuals to make the return trip to wholeness. Hopefully, the glow from this Big TOE will shed enough light to give both science and philosophy a rational first peek over the top of the PMR prison wall. Time will tell.

Thus, *My Big TOE* – obviously a work of metaphysics and philosophy – is by virtue of its methodology, rational process, logic, and careful experimentation, also a work of science. It is in a similar category (reality models) with the atomic shell model, string theory, or any other scientific model for that matter – only much larger in its scope. The data needed to validate this model must come from science, philosophy, and most importantly, from **your** objectively evaluated subjective experience.

The *My Big TOE* trilogy does indeed represent a serious scientific effort that is carefully and objectively investigating the reality that lies both within and without. With this science we have successfully derived, explained, and integrated the results of some of the world's best and most respected physicists. At the same time, we have explained mind, spirit and purpose, uniting the normal and the paranormal under one TOE – one consistent, logical, and rational understanding that explains **all** the data.

▶ This is the perfect place to take another short pause – this time, to round up the objective (shared) side of the Big TOE bottom line. We will focus on the subjective (personal) side of that bottom line a little later.

Even at the introductory level of a 101 survey course, *My Big TOE* provides a sound theoretical basis for understanding many of the scientific, metaphysical, theological, and philosophical enigmas that have been nagging at the minds of scholars and thinkers for decades. Even more importantly, *My Big TOE* provides a logical scientific basis for finally answering some of the most mysterious and pressing **personal** questions that have challenged human understanding since time immemorial – since men and women first stared into a starlit sky and wondered who and why they were.

If you dare to open your mind as well as your eyes and take a hard **objective** look at the world around you, you will find a plethora of solid, respectable, repeatable data points that clearly point to the existence of a larger reality that exists beyond our present understanding. Most of these scientific studies and carefully documented reports of paranormal happenings or other scientific enigmas (such as wave particle duality or entangled particle pairs) can be adequately explained, as well as given a solid theoretical basis, by applying the reality model presented in *My Big TOE*.

Many individuals have personal experiences that likewise point to the existence of a larger reality. *My Big TOE* provides the logical and rational understanding that is required to pull these experiences out of the closet of "weird things I experienced but don't understand and usually don't talk about," into the liberating light of a scientifically derived Big Picture.

With the understanding provided by *My Big TOE*, much of what we study, observe, and experience that has been beyond explanation and totally without a logical scientific basis, can now be seen as a natural part of the reality we live in, experience, and are a part of. All manner of things mysterious, both scientific and personal, that did not make sense before, make sense now.

How do you determine if a model (theory) is true and accurate? Ask these questions: Does it make sense out of what was previously not understandable? Does it explain **all** the data? Does it provide new direction, new perspectives, and new knowledge in a form that is both useful and profitable? Does it enable significant progress in your effort to understand yourself or the outside world more fully?

You must scientifically evaluate each of these questions relative to your subjective private world, and relatively to your objective public world. You are the final judge and it is your responsibility to find and develop the evidence that you need to judge wisely.

Here is the bottom line simply put. If *My Big TOE* delivers useful answers, if it rings true at the deepest level of your knowing, if it is verified by your research, your data, and your experience, if it helps you make sense of your life and your work, then raise it up. Use it as a tool for obtaining greater understanding and knowledge and for converting this new understanding and knowledge into wisdom. Be sure to tell others about the truths that you have discovered.

If, on the other hand, it fails to do these things for you, let it go. Let it stew in its own ineptitude; let it sink under the weight of its unprofitabiliy. Without lifting a finger, the ruthless dynamics of social and intellectual evolution will quickly cast aside any newcomer that rings false. Be sure to tell others about the falseness you have encountered.

In an intelligent and civilized society, ideas are allowed to compete in an open mental space with mutual respect and civility. A theory succeeds or fails by the degree of credibility invested in it by the established community that claims to be the experts, and by those who have applied the theory to good quality data and obtained valid results. In the best of worlds, these two groups should be composed of the same people; too often they are not.

Politics, power, personality, and science usually coalesce into the single abstruse voice of the scientific establishment. (In that last sentence feel free to replace the words "science" and "scientific" with the appropriate names of any group, profession, or organization. The dominating and dumbing influence of politics, power, and personality is as sadly ubiquitous as low quality consciousness.) Whatever the process, the fact remains: **Credibility must always be earned within the context of present understanding**.

Generally, this is a positive thing; social and intellectual viscosity slows the rate of change to ensure that carts stay behind horses – that knowledge does not get too far out ahead of wisdom. The pace of greater change reflects the pace of our greater learning. The world we live in is a direct expression of our collective quality. We are all responsible for the shared reality that we experience – it is our creation.

No idea will take root and blossom before its time, nor be denied when its time has come. To which side of that divide will *My Big TOE* fall? Readers, such as you, will collectively make that determination. *Que será, será.*◀

It would appear that these references and quotes are but the tip of an immense scientific and philosophical iceberg that is in fundamental consonance with *My Big TOE*. Big Truth is the same for everyone for all times; consequently it is not surprising that many of the worlds most brilliant minds, both past and present, should have discovered at least some part of it. I am certainly **not** trying to convince you to **believe** this or that by waving about a collection of quotes from a few of the world's most outstanding smart people.

I am equally sure one could find another assortment of smart people who would take the opposite view – one always can. Arguing that my smart people are smarter and more aware than your smart people is not exactly what I had in mind. That a million smart people say "yes" is not a good reason for **you** to say "yes" if you do not have the experience and understanding to support it. Determining truth is not a democratic process ruled by the majority. It is also not something that someone else can do for you. Do not let these smart people sway you to agree with them simply because they are smart. In fact, it is not a given that those I have quoted would support the merit of *My Big TOE*. They may agree or disagree, like it or disown it – that is not the point. These quotes are **not** presented as testimonials – that would be illogical as well as a misrepresentation.

The point here is to allow you to find some safety in numbers, some assurance that the ideas in *My Big TOE* are perhaps not the wild ravings of a single lone lunatic. It is a fact that there have been, and still are, many sober, serious, and very bright folks who have come to supportive and compatible (with *My Big TOE*) conclusions through the application of rigorous logic, mathematics, scientific principles, and careful rational study.

Another point is to demonstrate that perfectly competent, sane, and highly regarded scientists and thinkers can, and often do, hold well justified and thought out concepts that appear to be on or beyond the fringe relative to the normal attitudes and concepts held by the masses – even the masses of scientists and philosophers. All big discoveries (such as the spherical earth, the heliocentric solar system, the atom, quantum mechanics, and relativity) are initially shunned and held to be ridiculous by the great majority of scientists, philosophers, and other keepers of the cultural status quo and sacred belief systems. All of which brings to mind another famous quote from Albert Einstein: *"Great spirits have always encountered violent opposition from mediocre minds."*

And thus it shall ever be: Big ideas, innovation, and creativity always comes from the edge, never from the center. On the other hand, goofiness also comes from the edge, which is why those who are not competent to tell the difference huddle together for safety in the center. This brings us back to the concepts of the fear of not knowing, and finding safety in numbers. Therefore, dear reader, be assured that if you dare to travel near (or even beyond) the edge of acceptability as defined by the center, you may still be traveling in good company.

It is exceedingly rare, if not entirely impossible, for anything of deeper significance or importance to develop from, or within, the great majority living at the center – that is not their function. Nevertheless, the center is critically important because it provides stability and continuity, performs many necessary services, and provides the required infrastructure to maintain the whole. The center and the edge need each other in order to be a successful productive whole; each needs to learn to appreciate the other. The personal bottom line of this chapter is that you may live proudly and productively at the edge, appreciating the center, tolerating the indigenous goofiness found all around, fearlessly thinking Big-thoughts, and tasting the pudding.

It is a more satisfying life when we are living at a place on the continuum – from dead center to ragged edge – that is in consonance with our personality, nature, and capacity. Transitioning your home along that continuum always requires a difficult shift in your local reality.

I have purposely **not** mentioned the many wise persons who have come to conclusions in consonance with *My Big TOE* through means and processes other than Western scientific, mathematical, and rigorously logical methods. From this unmentioned group one could extract a mountain of wise and meaningful words – much of it from direct experience. Indeed, there is wonderful wisdom and insight that flows from all the great religions and spiritual traditions of the world. Though it may be tempting to provide quotes demonstrating a universal spiritual understanding throughout the ages that is supportive of the concepts developed within *My Big TOE*, this exposition does not come from that direction.

It is focused **at** the Western, scientific, logical, process-oriented mind, **by** a Western scientific, logical, process-oriented mind. To optimize its goal of successfully communicating to the growing intellectual products of Western culture, *My Big TOE* has built its logical structure solely upon a Western cultural foundation even if that foundation appears to many to be relatively impoverished in its understanding, acceptance, and experience of spiritual values. Things are often not as they appear; the average quality of consciousness in Western cultures is no less than the quality of consciousness found in other cultures. Tradition, ritual, and acceptance of an extant spiritual reality pays no automatic dividends in individual consciousness quality.

It is not that other than scientific contributions are not important, meaningful and significant, but that you must find those types of inputs on your own, according to your interests. I am not trying to develop a theology or start an argument. All I am doing here is sharing my direct experience and a few of the conclusions and possibilities that can be rationally derived from that experience. If that last sentence seems unlikely and difficult to fathom, it is because you do not share my experience.

The unintended conclusion of the above display of scientific and intellectual support for many of the concepts found within *My Big TOE* may be that the world is full of raving lunatics – that genius and insanity often travel together. You may also conclude that when a collection of sober and clear-headed people of sound intelligence and proven capability say something that you do not understand (sound like lunatics), it may be an error to jump immediately to the conclusion that they obviously do not understand the world as well as you do or that they are either stupid, delusional, or diabolical. Consider the outside possibility that there may be some other reason why you are having difficulty understanding what they are saying.

Unfortunately, open is not a normal state of mind. Admitting ignorance has always been un-cool – something no self-respecting ego would ever do without first being cornered by a mob.

To keep the record straight, lots of goofiness comes from the center as well, but it is a less obvious, more insidious, traditional form of goofiness that both reflects and is supported by the dominant culture (racism, sexism, slavery, witch hunts, religious fundamentalism, stifling conformity and intolerance, irrational fear of change, political correctness, conspicuous consumption, blue laws, grocery store tabloids, pet rocks, and beanie babies come immediately to mind).

You might as well accept it; this is simply the way we humans are. Our state of being accurately reflects the quality of our consciousness and the present extent of our evolution. As long as overgrown egos are the norm and as long as we have AUM derived consciousness at our core, the struggle will continue.

Our struggle is the struggle of an evolving digital consciousness driven by free will, existing in a state of continual becoming, trying to improve itself. We try to grow up, decrease our entropy, actualize the potential we inherit from AUM, and become one with the larger reality – aware in the outermost loop while maintaining individuality. Our struggle to evolve the quality of our consciousness is derived from AUM's struggle to evolve the quality of its consciousness.

It is the struggle of the edge with the middle and the middle with the edge. It is the struggle of fear and ignorance against love and understanding; of ego, wants and needs against compassion, humility and balance; of good against evil; of what you can get versus what you can give. This struggle forces every choice you make, every interaction that takes place within your experience, to fall to one side or the other.

What, dear reader, is **your** part in this epic struggle? Where do you fit in? What is the significance of you? And, if by some odd chance you are not exactly the same person who began reading *My Big TOE* some weeks ago, how long will it take you to return to normal – even if returning to normal is not your **present** stated intent?

For in the end, there is no end – only a beginning.

20

■ ■ ■

More Good Company

■ ■ ■

In this continuation of the previous chapter, I will not limit our traveling companions to **only** top scientists, mathematicians, and logic driven philosophers, of worldwide fame and stature. In this chapter, I will open the gates a little wider and also include some well known thinkers, artists, writers, political leaders, educators, and a few others – men and women of some renown who have earned reputations for the quality and soundness of their thoughts and deeds – all from our own Western culture.

Anyone I could associate with a known dogma or non-western culture was disqualified from this group, even if the words of these individuals non-dogmatically represented obvious truth and wisdom. Why be that restrictive? The *My Big TOE* trilogy is focused on those immersed within a worldwide Western culture. Unfortunately, most people feel uncomfortable with, and subsequently discount, information coming from a culture other than their own. Most people do not trust information from an unfamiliar source. My restrictiveness is merely an act of straightforward pragmatism – I am simply trying to communicate effectively with the largest number of readers. Please take no offense if I pass over one or more of your favorite wise persons.

A casual inspection of a few Internet quote repositories has produced more than enough material to make the point that many of the thoughts and attitudes expressed in *My Big TOE* are not as far off the beaten path as you might have first thought. By now, this should be an expected result. From whatever direction you approach fundamental truth, the result is the same once differences in personal expression are accounted for.

Actually, the West is not as spiritually bankrupt as it appears; it simply lacks a widely acceptable mode of expression of spiritual values at the cultural level. However, because the quality of consciousness is a personal matter, the lack of a pervasive cultural expression is irrelevant. The lack of a serious pervasive cultural sense of a bigger picture has its benefits as well as drawbacks.

> ▶ I hear some objections to my statement that the West lacks solid spiritual values at the cultural level. There are some spiritual values shallowly embedded within Western culture, but these have mostly been reduced to effete slogans hanging like window dressing on the edge of the dominant religious dogma – they orchestrate little cultural force at a deep level. Why? Because in Western culture there is a huge, nearly unbridgeable gap between the physical and the nonphysical, between being and doing, between I and other, and between the theory and practice of spiritual values.
>
> The large majority of **religious** values have little, if anything, to do with **spiritual** values. This is as true in the East as it is in the West. ◀

This chapter should be fun. Now that the conceptual heavy lifting has been done, I think you will enjoy this relaxed cool-down meander through the intellectual fields of Western sound bite wisdom – a collection of thoughtful gems that bear repeating. I have broken the material into several groups and will say a few words about how each set of quotes relates to *My Big TOE*.

Belief and Self-Imposed Limitations

This set of sound bites speaks to the power of belief to insulate the believer from additional knowledge or finding a larger truth – a point made repetitively in *My Big TOE*. Here, you will also find corroboration that most people have a natural tendency to feel that they know more than they do – that if **they** do not know it, if **they** have not experienced it; it is not likely to be true. These folks are sure that if they and their peer group have no direct experience of a larger reality, the larger reality must be the product of delusion. (The delusional always believe that they are non-delusional and that the non-delusional are delusional – such is the nature of delusion).

Many of Western culture, scientists in particular, are snared in this "arrogance by assumed omniscience" belief trap. It was this same inflated sense of self – that only **other** people could be largely ignorant – that led some of the most respected scientists of the early 1900s to laugh confidently at a young and foolish Albert Einstein for presenting his obviously incorrect theory of relativity. Einstein magnanimously tolerated many arrogant and unkind professional guffaws before getting the last laugh.

As you can see from this first quote, Albert had no use for those caught in the vision limiting belief trap of: "If this doesn't make sense to **me**, then it must be wrong." For those following the well-worn path (steadfastly trod by the large majority in the conceptual center) of common belief masquerading as common knowledge, Dr. Einstein had this to say:

"He who joyfully marches in rank and file has already earned my contempt. He has been given a large brain by mistake, since for him the spinal cord would suffice."

Wow, those are strong words! Quite uncharacteristic of the famously kind and gentle Einstein. Albert had obviously been badly burned a few times by professional and personal know-it-all arrogance.

This lack of appreciation of the extent of your ignorance, and the belief that you already know almost everything important – that what is unknown is small compared to what is known – is usually laid at the feet of common sense. I hear muttering from the intellectuals in the conceptual center – from those who maintain the cultural status quo and staunchly defend our most sacred cultural beliefs:

"Even if I cannot **prove** the absolute truth of our shared cultural assumptions and beliefs, nevertheless, it is only good common sense that **no** reality exists beyond PMR, that we are **not** individuated consciousness experiencing a virtual physical reality, and that a digitally based consciousness is an **obvious** impossibility. Clearly, this Big-TOE-thing is a heap of misguided bullpucky borne of fuzzy wishful thinking and bad science. Why, the logical flaws are so obvious that I do not have to point them out – anyone with half a brain could refute these misguided arguments. Everyone knows that mysticism is dim-witted nonsense that lesser minds use to indulge their inherent weakness."

These attitudes reflect the common sense view of most contemporary westerners, including scientists. Again, it was Albert Einstein who was on the receiving end of a great deal of common sense – enough to prompt him to pen this quip:

"Common sense is the collection of prejudices acquired by age eighteen."

Einstein was not the only one to feel the pressure of cultural conformity; many others also understood the power of belief to create the world in its own image and to reduce thinking to the recitation of current fashion within the politically correct center.

"People see the world not as it is, but as they are."
— AL LEE

"People see only what they are prepared to see."
— RALPH WALDO EMERSON

"If one does not understand a person, one tends to regard him as a fool."
— CARL JUNG

"The truth which makes men free is for the most part
the truth which men prefer not to hear."
— HERBERT AGAR (*A Time for Greatness* [1942])

"The conventional view serves to protect us
from the painful job of thinking."
— J. K. GALBRAITH

"Men occasionally stumble over the truth, but most of them pick
themselves up and hurry off as if nothing had happened."
— WINSTON CHURCHILL

"To a very large extent men and women are a product
of how they define themselves. As a result of a combination of innate
ideas and the intimate influences of the culture and environment we grow
up in, we come to have beliefs about the nature of being human.
These beliefs penetrate to a very deep level of our psychosomatic systems,
our minds and brains, our nervous systems, our endocrine systems,
and even our blood and sinews. We act, speak, and think
according to these deeply held beliefs and belief systems."
— JEREMY W. HAYWARD

"The world we see that seems so insane is the result of a belief system
that is not working. To perceive the world differently, we must be
willing to change our belief system, let the past slip away,
expand our sense of now, and dissolve the fear in our minds."
— GERALD G. JAMPOLSKY

"Whatever one believes to be true either is true
or becomes true in one's mind."
— JOHN C. LILLY

"When we argue for our limitations, we get to keep them."
— PETER MCWILLIAMS

"Nothing is so firmly believed as that which we least know."
— MICHEL EYQUEM DE MONTAIGNE

"Skeptic does not mean him who doubts, but him who investigates or researches, as opposed to him who asserts and thinks that he has found."
— MIGUEL DE UNAMUNO

"Illusions commend themselves to us because they save us pain and allow us to enjoy pleasure instead. We must therefore accept it without complaint when they sometimes collide with a bit of reality against which they are dashed to pieces."
— SIGMUND FREUD

"The pursuit of truth will set you free; even if you never catch up with it."
— CLARENCE DARROW

"People demand freedom of speech as a compensation for the freedom of thought which they seldom use."
— KIERKEGAARD

"Thoughts have power; thoughts are energy. And you can make your world or break it by your own thinking."
— SUSAN TAYLOR

"There is nothing more frightful than ignorance in action."
— GOETHE

*"Nothing is easier than self-deceit.
For what each man wishes,
that he also believes to be true."*
— DEMOSTHENES

*"If you don't change your beliefs, your life will be like this forever.
Is that good news?"*
— DR. ROBERT ANTHONY

Mysticism, Ideas from the Edge

To many in Western culture it is perfectly clear and only common sense that anything connected to metaphysics or mysticism is pure unadulterated nonsense. To the well-educated Westerner, it is obvious that such fools and their delusions have preyed on the gullibility of the uneducated masses since the beginning of time. Let me pass on some advice from the conceptual center:

"An intelligent well-educated person would be well-advised to stay clear of deluded individuals or risk losing their credibility by association. Even if these confused mystics are well meaning, and not simply hustlers and charlatans, their silly gibber-jabber flies in the face of science and makes no sense. The paranormal, mysticism, and 'miracles' are mental and emotional pacifiers for the dumb, the uneducated, the emotionally needy, and the gullible."

Do you know anybody who thinks like that? Forty years ago almost everyone centered in Western culture thought like that. Now these cultural and scientific mental straight jackets (beliefs) are worn only by a large majority – the edge has grown ever so slightly amid a greater tolerance of individuality. Einstein evidently knew many individuals who clung to their rational hard-science *über alles* belief systems like a very young child clings to its favorite teddy bear. Much of his writings indicate that he found such people to be extremely limited and boorish – lacking both intelligence and imagination.

> "The most beautiful thing we can experience is the mysterious.
> It is the source of all true art and science."
> — ALBERT EINSTEIN

> "There are only two ways to live your life. One is as though nothing is a
> miracle. The other is as though everything is a miracle."
> — ALBERT EINSTEIN

> "The important thing is not to stop questioning.
> Curiosity has its own reasons for existing. One cannot help but be in awe
> when he contemplates the mysteries of eternity, of life, of the marvelous
> structure of reality. It is enough if one tries to comprehend
> a little of this mystery every day. Never lose a holy curiosity."
> — ALBERT EINSTEIN

"What our eyes behold may well be the text of life but one's meditations
on the text and the disclosures of these meditations are no less
a part of the structure of reality."
— WALLACE STEVENS

"The foundations of a person are not in matter but in spirit."
— RALPH WALDO EMERSON

As I explained in Section 2, logic requires that a successful Big TOE (as opposed to a little PMR-only TOE) must have at least one seemingly mystical assumption. That mystical assumption appears mystical only from the limited perspective of PMR. *My Big TOE* is constructed entirely from two assumptions; 1) the seemingly mystical one: the existence of primordial consciousness (AUO); and 2) the well known and understood Fundamental Process of evolution. From just those two ingredients, all reality flows, including the relatively small but interesting subset of the larger reality we experience as PMR.

"The grand aim of all science is to cover the greatest number
of empirical facts by logical deduction from the
smallest number of hypotheses or axioms."
— ALBERT EINSTEIN

Elegant simplicity is the hallmark of Big Truth. According to Einstein, elegant simplicity is also the grand aim of all science. Combining both ideas logically provides that Big Truth is the grand aim of all science. Tell that to all the little picture scientists who have no interest in Big Truth. In its pursuit of Big Truth, *My Big TOE*, employs the elegant simplicity of a single consciousness-evolution fractal ecosystem to derive All That Is, science and philosophy, point and purpose from two simple assumptions.

The Process and Importance of Growth
Within *My Big TOE*, I describe personal growth – the improvement of the quality of your consciousness – as the point of your existence. It is the evolutionary urge of the Fundamental Process applied to consciousness that pushes us forward to evolve the quality of our being – to lower our entropy. It is growth – spiritual growth – that links us to AUM, defines the

positive direction of progress, and gives us purpose and meaning within the Big Picture. If ever there were a law of being and existence, it would be: Grow or die. Stability lies only in growth, maintaining the status quo is the first sign of impending decay. Growth is the point, the purpose, what makes the experiment run, and the reason for going on. When consciousness and evolution become entangled, modification toward improvement is the result – growth defines the struggle to be. Without growth, without an opportunity to evolve our being, we are nothing.

> *"The self is only that which is in the process of becoming."*
> — SØREN KIERKEGAARD

> *"What is the most rigorous law of our being? Growth. No smallest atom of our moral, mental, or physical structure can stand still a year. It grows – it must grow; nothing can prevent it."*
> — MARK TWAIN

> *"Unless you try to do something beyond what you have mastered, you will never grow."*
> — C.R. LAWTON

> *"One's mind, once stretched by a new idea, never regains its original dimensions."*
> — OLIVER WENDELL HOLMES

> *"Only in growth, reform, and change, paradoxically enough, is true security to be found."*
> — ANNE MORROW LINDBERGH

Einstein realized that in the atomic age, the spiritual growth of mankind had suddenly become more critical – that the age-old struggle of raising the quality of consciousness would now take on more urgency.

> *"The release of atomic energy has not created a new problem. It has merely made more urgent the necessity of solving an existing one."*
> — ALBERT EINSTEIN

Little did he know that mankind would devise several additional ways to destroy life on our planet within a few decades. Given this destructive capacity, future human genetic engineering, psychotropic pharmaceuticals, and the coming Information Age, it has never been more important for mankind to understand the Big Picture before it prematurely terminates this portion of The Great Experiment in Consciousness.

"What lies behind us and what lies before us
are tiny matters compared to what lies within us."
— OLIVER WENDELL HOLMES

Wisdom

Many times within the pages of *My Big TOE*, we have struggled with the problem of separating the truly wise from the delusional fools that would try to appear wise – separating knowledge from pseudo-knowledge, and truth from belief. We concluded that a careful results oriented exploration with plenty of pauses to taste the pudding would be the best process. Wisdom, we said, was derived only from experience and reflects an appreciation and understanding of the Big Picture.

Unfortunately, only the wise can understand and confidently apply wisdom to their reality. Because it takes one to know one, a relatively slow incremental bootstrapping process is required to become wise or to recognize and appreciate the wisdom of others. Because wisdom is non-transferable, only you can decide who are fools and who are wise – and only for yourself. We said that **your** wisdom must flow from **your** experience and that it could not be acquired from psychotropic chemicals, a book, or a guru. We said that wisdom was the natural result of a high quality of consciousness. It seems that others agree with many of these ideas.

"Never mistake knowledge for wisdom. One helps you
make a living; the other helps you make a life."
— SANDRA CAREY

"It requires wisdom to understand wisdom:
the music is nothing if the audience is deaf."
— WALTER LIPPMAN

"Wisdom is not wisdom when it is derived from books alone."
— HORACE

"Try not to become a man of success, but rather
try to become a man of value."
— ALBERT EINSTEIN

"We can be knowledgeable with other men's knowledge,
but we cannot be wise with other men's wisdom."
— MICHEL DE MONTAIGNE

Fear, Ego, and Delusion

In a long aside in Chapter 8, Book 2, we discuss the interrelationships that exist among fear, ego, intellect, ignorance, and delusion. From this unholy combination it was reasoned that most of our daily problems emerge as self-inflicted wounds. We saw how fear and ignorance prompted a mutual support alliance between the ego and intellect to deny the fear by constructing a personal fantasy (belief system). We watched the pathetic self struggle to maintain the ego's delusion, only to become enslaved by the maintenance requirements of its own deceit. Fear, the opposite of love, was shown to be the root of most everyone's personal problems as well as the main inhibitor of improving the quality of consciousness.

"Fear defeats more people than any other one thing in the world."
— RALPH WALDO EMERSON

"An inflated consciousness is always egocentric and conscious
of nothing but its own existence. It is incapable of learning from the past,
incapable of understanding contemporary events, and incapable of
drawing right conclusions about the future. It is hypnotized by itself
and therefore cannot be argued with. It inevitably dooms itself
to calamities that must strike it dead."
— CARL JUNG

"To understand the world, one must not be worrying about one's self."
— ALBERT EINSTEIN

Truth, Science, and Logic

In Sections 2, 3, and 5 we make a case for expanding the purview of science to include a wider range of phenomena. We explain how the PMR-only view of reality eliminates the possibility of seeing the bigger picture – how it unnecessarily limits the available solution space so that important scientific problems appear to be mysterious and unsolvable. Many for a long time have known the fact that understanding the larger reality requires a vision and perspective that goes beyond our normal sense of PMR. It is no secret that we are intellectually trapped by the limitations of our little picture beliefs about reality; and that there is much more to existence than the local causal physics of PMR.

Likewise, it is clear that rational knowledge, causality, and formal scientific process must rise above its present intellectual little picture entrapment to illuminate the truth that lies beyond simple physical existence. However, it is important to understand that explorations of consciousness also need the rigor of a more general scientific process to separate truth from fiction, the actual from the apparent, the meaningful and significant from the useless and unimportant.

Scientific methodology is not to be abandoned to superstition – in fact, it is exactly the opposite. Scientific methodology needs to rise above the superstition and belief that now cripples its vision in order to separate truth from fiction at a higher level of rational understanding. Personal explorations of consciousness into NPMR are not about otherwise intelligent people (including scientists) becoming mush-heads in PMR – it is more about self-limited PMR boneheads becoming scientists at the next higher level of causality.

"As far as the laws of mathematics refer to reality, they are not certain;
and as far as they are certain, they do not refer to reality."
— ALBERT EINSTEIN

"We should take care not to make the intellect our god; it has,
of course, powerful muscles, but no personality."
— ALBERT EINSTEIN

"The significant problems we face cannot be solved at the same level
of thinking we were at when we created them."
— ALBERT EINSTEIN

"Not everything that can be counted counts,
and not everything that counts can be counted."
— ALBERT EINSTEIN

"The further the spiritual evolution of mankind advances,
the more certain it seems to me that the path to genuine religiosity
does not lie through the fear of life, and the fear of death, and blind
faith, but through striving after rational knowledge."
— ALBERT EINSTEIN

*"Every great advance in science
has issued from a new audacity of imagination."*
— JOHN DEWEY, THE QUEST FOR CERTAINTY

*"There is one thing even more vital to science than intelligent methods;
and that is, the sincere desire to find out the truth, whatever it may be."*
— CHARLES SANDERS PIERCE

*"We must learn to tailor our concepts to fit reality,
instead of trying to stuff reality into our concepts."*
— VICTOR DANIELS

Education, Learning and Personal Growth

We said that growth is what life is all about, the point of your existence, the reason for being here, but how does this growth happen? How do you go about growing up? We know that fear and ego block learning and personal growth. Certainly, everyone will agree that growing-up is more a being process than an intellectual process.

Essentially, success is a matter of perspective, attitude, vision, perseverance, and the gumption to get out there and try – and then try again. All you need is a glimpse of the possibilities and the determination to explore at least some of those possibilities. Perhaps, if you are ready, willing, and able, *My Big TOE* will help you see some new tantalizing possibilities. However, supplying the necessary gumption and determination is all up to you – no one can help you with that.

Your intent reflects the quality of your being and drives your choices. It is learning and personal growth that eventually enable you to make the right choices for the right reasons – naturally and intuitively. Every day of every year we are forced to make hundreds of significant choices as we interact with others. We express ourselves with choice. We paint ourselves onto the canvas of the actualized present with brushes of intent and pigments of choice. We juggle a thousand shades of competing need, fear, ego, desire, understanding, compassion, humility, caring and love in a swirling mix of contradiction until it all coalesces into a single result that is actualized into the present irreversible reality by the choices we make. We are the sum total of those choices made over a lifetime, or a series of lifetimes. The substance of our being and the rate of our growth are defined by the quality of our choices.

*"One's philosophy is not best expressed in words;
it's expressed in the choices one makes. In the long run,
we shape our lives and we shape ourselves. The process never ends
until we die. And the choices we make are ultimately our responsibility."*
— ELEANOR ROOSEVELT

Learning, like growth, is a personal thing – it is generated from the inside out. If we try to educate another by stuffing knowledge in from the outside, like stuffing tissue in a bra, we can achieve only the appearance of education – produce an educated falsie. Our school systems have, during the last century, essentially abandoned education in favor of force-feeding factual information and developing the bare essentials of a functional literacy. Education should never be confused with training. Unfortunately, in our culture most people would be hard pressed to explain the difference.

It is no wonder that the intellectual center is predominately populated by well-educated, well-credentialed, conceptually limited, original-thinking challenged preservers of the status quo. It is also no wonder that so few of us have the inclination and drive to pursue Big Truth on the Path of Knowledge.

*"You cannot teach a man anything;
you can only help him find it within himself."*
— GALILEO

*"Education is what remains after one has
forgotten everything he learned in school."*
— ALBERT EINSTEIN

*"I find that the great thing in this world is not so much where we stand
as in what direction we are moving; To reach the port of heaven,
we must sail sometimes with the wind and sometimes against it –
but we must sail, and not drift, nor lie at anchor."*
— OLIVER WENDELL HOLMES

*"Knowing is not enough; we must apply.
Willing is not enough; we must do."*
— GOETHE

"Everybody wants to be somebody; nobody wants to grow."
— GOETHE

Growing up is never an easy or quick process. Anxiety and **internal** struggle is always generated when abandoning comfortable and familiar ways of being, thinking, and believing. Diving headlong into the unfamiliar and murky waters of something new and different comes with no guarantee of success. Additionally, there are the **external** struggles with being different – a stranger among your friends – living near the edge in a world dominated by those in the center. Growing up takes great courage as well as great determination.

"Great spirits have always found violent opposition from mediocrities.
The latter cannot understand it when a man does not
thoughtlessly submit to hereditary prejudices but honestly and
courageously uses his intelligence."
— ALBERT EINSTEIN

"What we need is not the will to believe, but the wish to find out."
— BERTRAND RUSSELL

"The journey to happiness involves finding the courage to go down into
ourselves and take responsibility for what's there: all of it."
— RICHARD ROHR

"All life is an experiment."
– RALPH WALDO EMERSON

"Happiness is not a reward – it is a consequence.
Suffering is not a punishment – it is a result."
— ROBERT GREEN INGERSOLL

Seeing the Big Picture, understanding the larger reality, growing up, increasing the quality or synergy of your consciousness, evolving your consciousness, decreasing the entropy of your consciousness, spiritual growth – or whatever you want to call it – is your responsibility and yours alone. If you are waiting for progress to come to you, or need a growth path that is easy and requires little effort, or cannot stand to be very different from your peers, or require certainty before you can take a step, or are simply stuck in a belief trap of some sort, you are not irretrievably lost. When you are ready, an opportunity to grow will become visible.

Time in PMR is an experience defined by the perception of change. Your deluded perception of a short, somewhat random, existence on planet earth does not limit your responsibility for growth. Every decision, intent, motivation, and action moves you along one way or another in the Big Picture whether you are aware that you are participating in an iterative repeat it until you get it consciousness-quality learning lab or not.

Fortunately, the majority of us are growing more or less in the positive direction. The major difference your effort is likely to make is to increase dramatically the rate of your progress and the quality of your existence. That's all. No big deal if you are enjoying your current level of consciousness quality – this is not a timed test. You can accomplish only whatever you are ready for, and capable of. If you decide to kick back and let your opportunities for growth slip by unexplored, one note of caution: Don't let the anti-rats (defined in Chapter 2, Book 2) get you. They primarily prey on the slackers and stragglers. But don't worry; I am sure that won't be a problem for you. Come on along when you are ready.

I have shown you the Big Picture and told you how it works, but I cannot cause you to integrate it into your knowledge-base at a level that is deeper than your intellect.

I have enabled you to see and feel some of the potential that you have as a chip from the old AUM block, but only you can actualize that potential.

As your tour guide, I have pointed out some of the more interesting sights, but you have to get off the intellectual tour bus and experience them on your own.

I have provided a dim glimmer of the possibilities that lie before your being, but you must provide the courage and determination to pursue that vision to some personally profitable conclusion.

I have provided a model of reality to help you interpret, structure, and add rational meaning to your personal experience, but you have to have the experience and then learn from it.

I have pointed out some of the mental and conceptual limitations and constraints that bind you and blind you, but only you can set yourself free and extend your vision.

I have told you some Big Truths, but they must remain vague and powerless until you find them for yourself.

I have explained to you how spirituality, consciousness, love, and paranormal phenomena are interconnected, but I cannot cause you to directly experience any of them.

I have encouraged you with sticks and carrots and pointed you in the right general direction, but I cannot define your personal path much less carry you down it.

I have explained why you are here and what the point and meaning of both your physical and nonphysical existence is, but you must express your own intent and make your own choices in order to make that existence significant and successful.

I have done what I can do. The ball is in your court. How you play it, how the concepts you have found within *My Big TOE* interact with, and ultimately affect, the quality of your being, is entirely up to you. However you currently express your quality and intent – however you make the important choices – if you make them with a long term vigorous, open minded, and skeptical commitment to the relentless pursuit of Big Truth, you will eventually succeed. Who you are, what you experience, and the reality you create, are the applied results of whatever Big Truth you have managed to capture and internalize. What could be more straightforward than that? Good consciousness quality is the result of an open mind, a focused steady intent, and the courage to be.

I know what you are thinking: Easy to say, difficult to do. Sometimes growing the quality of your consciousness doesn't seem particularly straightforward or simple because you are exploring unfamiliar territory. The unknown always appears tricky whether it is or not. New paradigms always seem impossible before they become obvious and trivial. If you "just go do it" with a long-term view, seemingly impenetrable barriers will begin to dissolve before your steady unconditional effort. If you never go do it or give up easily because those barriers seem to be hopelessly impenetrable – they will be.

I hope you have had a few valuable insights as well as a few good laughs as we have explored some of the territory that lies beyond the edge of your everyday thoughts. Adventures of mind and spirit are best absorbed in alternating doses of work and play – an interweaving of light and heavy. Learning and growing, once past the boot-camp phase, should be joyful and fun. If you have been swinging a pick in a spiritual salt mine with little to show for it, you are wasting your time on technique, form, and process. That Big Truth yields best to pain, abstention, renunciation, suffering, and sacrifice is pure horsepucky. The Western Puritan ethic and the Western work ethic may combine to produce successful model citizens and productive workers on the outside, but they invariably lead to poverty and frustration on the inside.

Dedication does not mean work, work, work, work until you drop, succeed, quit, or give up the possibility. Dress up the Western work ethic in a monk's robe and you get more anxiety and frustration than spiritual progress. Big Truth is much more likely to yield to loving, lighthearted play than to the stiff ossified narrowness that often defines the mature and dignified Western approach. When happy children laugh and play they live closer to the core of existence – as they grow up and get appropriately serious, they lose their innocence and their intuitive harmony with The One. To be able to freely and seamlessly mix and intermingle knowledge, wisdom, and play is one of the gifts of enlightenment.

The darkness of ignorance surrounds all of us, all the time – we will probably never know all the answers there are to know. Will a bacterium ever become president of the United States? The idea of limitations does not come easy for us Westerners who habitually think in terms of physical objects and processes. Some barriers may need to be gracefully accepted – at least for a while, and maybe forever. Running with the herds of AUMosaurus thundering across the mental plains is simply beyond our capacities and purpose. Regardless, we will and should struggle to understand whatever is within our grasp. If we do not use our full capacity or reach our full potential, shame on us. If we reach limits, let's make sure that they are actual limits, not self-imposed limits. Let's make sure that darkness never becomes a thing in itself, but rather only the absence of light. For no one is ever fearful of the absence of light.

As your awareness evolves from dim to bright, it illuminates more and more of the Big Picture and pushes back the darkness that marks the boundaries of your personal knowing. As a conscious being imbued with the capacities and potential of your source, an ability to expand the light and grow the quality of your consciousness creates the challenge that your existence is all about.

Do not let the magnitude of these Big Picture concepts overwhelm you. We get to where we are going by patiently taking one step at a time. There is no other way – it is the same for everyone. Each of us follows a unique path that is defined as we go, one step at a time, by our free will driven intent. The key is to begin stepping out with a purposeful intent.

If I have succeeded in turning on lights here and there to challenge a few of your personal dark places, I am greatly pleased – but **you** must open your eyes and see what is (and is not) there for yourself. Then you must evaluate what you see – you must separate your personal truth from your personal delusion. The passageway to an improved quality of being lies along the path where personal truth and absolute truth eventually become one.

Recall that absolute truth (Big Truth) is universal and never changes; also that Big Truth is not secretively hidden away where only the chosen few can find it. To the contrary, Big Truth demonstrates itself right in front of your eyes and stares you in the face every day. Its discovery challenges you because your conscious awareness is dimmed and limited by your beliefs to such an extent that you shut yourself off from the experience you need to grow wisdom and more fully understand the bigger picture.

> *"What one has not experienced, one will never understand in print."*
> — ISADORA DUNCAN, *MY LIFE*

If you do not yet see light glowing from the possibilities within the bigger consciousness picture, I would hope that you would at least have a dim glimmer of where and how you can find the light-switch on your own in the event you one day get the urge and the courage to explore beyond the tiny little corner of virtual physical existence within which you have walled-off your awareness. Oh, but to lie safe and comfortable in the protective lap of a favorite belief trap – no challenge, no anxiety, no risk, no effort, and no growth – but with lots and lots of reassuring company that occupies itself justifying its beliefs and polishing up the status quo in an endless loop of self-referential ego-boosting blather. That sounds like a comfy and supportive place to live doesn't it? Such an existence – the very definition of normal – goes nowhere significant in the Big Picture, but is safe, easy, reassuring, and often materially rewarding in the little picture.

On the other hand, if you at least dimly grasp that you are a prisoner of your beliefs, confined to a tiny PMR cell of your own making, if you are vaguely aware there is something real beyond the experience of your five physical senses, perhaps now is the time to begin plotting your escape. Escaping belief traps and finding the necessary mental and emotional freedom to evaluate your experience logically and rationally will become your first-level quest. You will need to be daring and courageous. I am not suggesting an imaginary escape from the supposed real (physical) world – quite the contrary. I propose a real escape from the virtual world of PMR to a larger (superset) world that is closer to The Source and nearer to the core of fundamental existence – one that has an operational effect, and a measurable impact upon PMR – one that fulfills and sustains your deepest purpose as an aware evolving consciousness.

You are what you are – why not become all that you can be? How can you possibly discover what the limits of your being are without reaching beyond where you are now? How far, how consistently, and how steadily will you reach out toward the light of Big Truth? How courageously, carefully, honestly, and scientifically will you explore your personal unknown, your personal ignorance, prejudices, assumptions, fears, and beliefs? Are you ready, willing, and able to challenge the monster that lives under your bed at night? Do you need assurances and expect or require definitive answers to come quickly – or are you prepared to let the process take a lifetime and define its own path?

What's a lifetime worth? What else would you want to use one for? To see how much stuff or power you could accumulate, or how many facts you could figure out or learn? How about to see how much fun you could have, or how much beer you could drink? Perhaps all existence is random and the concepts of consciousness, evolution, entropy reduction, love, personal growth, and profitability are simply delusions because there can be no point or purpose in randomness. Does this feel right to you? What does **your intuition** say about there being significance, pattern and purpose to existence? What is **your** lifetime likely to be worth? (Please, don't bother asking your intellect – it will most likely only confuse you because it will **always** have insufficient data for a logical conclusion.) Even if your intuition is grossly underdeveloped, it is still a better guesser of Big Answers than your intellect. Don't worry; your skepticism will keep you safe until your intuition becomes certifiably reliable.

To help you answer these questions, I have offered you a unified theory of existence and reality, a comprehensive TOE, and a reasonably detailed model of reality-mechanics based upon my own carefully evaluated explorations of the larger reality. The extent to which you have actually absorbed **useful** understanding at a deep level has at least as much, if not more, to do with you, your beliefs, and your experience than it does with the correctness of My Big Picture Theory Of Everything. Think about that; read that last sentence again. Your consciousness, its quality, your awareness, and your reality are intertwined in the Big Picture – their apparent separateness as independent entities is a PMR-based illusion that helps you maintain your focus on the basic things you need to learn first.

> *"Truth can never be told so as to be understood, and not be believed."*
> — WILLIAM BLAKE

If you wish to progress beyond the bottom rung of knowing – which simply is to be a believer – you must develop your own personal understanding and truth. Perhaps *My Big TOE* has provided some of the fertile ground that you need to create and grow **your** Big TOE. Perhaps it has given you some support and encouragement, or merely goaded you to think about and assess your personal truth. If *My Big TOE* has caused you to ponder at least a few big thoughts, then we have had a successful journey together. Whether the thoughts that are rattling around in your head today are in close agreement or strong disagreement with the model I have presented makes little difference. As long as you continue to probe, ponder, and seek Big Truth open mindedly, you will eventually find it.

Everyone has at least a stub of a Big TOE – whether it is by purposeful construction or by cultural default, whether it is right or wrong, helpful or useless, belief-based and fearful, or love-based and all encompassing. For most, it is a reflection of their core beliefs – their worldview at the bone and sinew level. For others it represents the result of a lifetime of experience and careful intellectual effort, or perhaps a mindless acquiescence to social, religious, scientific, and cultural norms. However well or poorly your stubby (or grand) Big TOE is defined, it is the place where you must start if you wish to grow it beyond its present state. Leave the giant leaps to lottery winners and mythical heroes – consistent plodding in the generally right direction is a better and surer way to get to where you want to go. A personal growth strategy that primarily depends on good luck or some special connection (book, guru, technique, ritual, belief system) for success is little more than a procrastinator's excuse or the common fantasy of those who lack the gumption, self-discipline, or understanding to succeed on their own.

Consciousness, by its nature, is nonphysical (from a PMR point of view) and personal. As an individuated consciousness you create your own local reality that has both shared (objective and PMR-rule-based) and personal (subjective and NPMR-rule-based) components at all levels of awareness.

How closely your personal reality expresses Big Truth determines the quality and the correctness of any Big TOE based upon that personal reality. Each individual must **personally** discover Big Truth. If Big Truth is not discovered (primarily a subjective process) and applied and tested (primarily an objective process) by means of your personal experience, its concept, if known at all, can reside only in your intellect as a relatively powerless theoretical idea.

The personal power and wisdom of a high-quality consciousness must be derived through your personal experience of that consciousness. Intellectual transfers of information and factual understanding can do little more than point your intent in the right direction. Nonetheless, the purposeful direction of intent by a free will can be an exceedingly powerful tool. The good news is that profitable growth experience always follows steady, serious, and well-directed intent. The intellect, though poorly understood and badly misused, does have a valued place and function in the evolutionary process of growing consciousness quality. You were born with everything you need to succeed. The only items you must bring to the table are the personal will, drive, courage, and intent to pursue and find Big Truth. If you have those, everything else will fall into place.

Well, that's it ladies and gentlemen, boys and girls, men and women, and the rest of you who fit better under some other category – you are now on your own. Actually, you always have been on your own, but now you should have at least a glimmer of the Big Picture, a better appreciation of the possibilities available to you, and some idea of how to go about actualizing those possibilities if you decide that is what you want to do.

As *My Big TOE*, the book, comes to an end, it is my intent that these quotes and comments have given you some final clarity, direction, and understanding as they wrap-up the **personal** bottom-line of Big-TOEness and provide some assurance that if you do decide to pursue the Path of Knowledge, you will be traveling in good company. Be assured it is not only religious fundamentalists and freelance kooks who are pursuing a bigger picture beyond physical reality. There are plenty of those to be sure, but there are also plenty of seekers with keen analytical minds and careful processes who are making real progress toward actualizing themselves within a larger reality, who are purposely evolving their quality and moving toward regaining their natural capacities as aware individuated portions of AUM consciousness, who are gaining and productively utilizing the awesome power and value of a balanced reduced-entropy consciousness. You can be among them if you care enough to "just do it." You have the capability and potential required for success – you are not excluded by any force or barrier other than what **you** create.

> ▶ Where one journey ends, another must begin. I won't be traveling with you on your next journey. I have no idea where you are headed, or where you will end up but I do have one little question about how you are going to make the trip. Will you be 1) in charge and driving, 2) along for the ride in the passenger's seat, 3) locked in the trunk, or 4) dragged, kicking and screaming, at the end of a rope?
> Bon voyage, amigo! Have a nice trip…. and may you graduate from boot-camp before the rope breaks. ◀

Ah, yes, the fun is never done, but the public unraveling of this particular Big TOE is at its end. Because you have been patient enough to read this strange trilogy all the way to the end, I have come up with a small going away present for you. When and if you decide to go traveling into inner space, I will help you out with all the necessary accommodations – well, that is, as long as you don't require mints placed on your pillow. When and if you begin to understand your existence as consciousness – when you begin exploring the Big Picture that lies on the other side of your mind – when you start experimenting with the larger reality of NPMR and its inhabitants – well…, just tell 'em that ol' Uncle Tom sent you – they'll take good care of you, show you around, and see to it that you stay out of trouble. I'll leave the lights on for you.

Find the other two books of the *My Big TOE* trilogy:
http://www.My-Big-TOE.com
http://www.lightningstrikebooks.com
Phone orders: 1-800-901-2122